HOW WELL DO YOU KNOW
ANGLESEY?

How well do you know ANGLESEY?

A quiz book by
Margaret Hughes

© Text: Margaret Hughes

ISBN: 978-1-84524-118-6

Cover design: Sian Parri

First edition: 2008
Llygad Gwalch, Ysgubor Plas, Llwyndyrys,
Pwllheli, Gwynedd LL53 6NG
☎ 01758 750432   📠 01758 750438
✆ lona@carreg-gwalch.com   Website: www.carreg-gwalch.com

How well do you know Anglesey?

To know the island one needs to know something of its past, the landscape and seascape and its people. For Anglesey is not merely a beautiful island. It is rich in history and legend, it has produced some remarkable characters, it is a vibrant society, proud of its past but looking eagerly to its future.

As the text of this book is English, English place-names have been used where appropriate. The original Welsh names are the subject of one of the questions.

Where there is a reference to the town now called 'Menai Bridge' in English, before 1826 when the Suspension Bridge was opened to traffic, the original name of 'Porthaethwy' is used.

Test your knowledge here. Learn as you check your answers. Enjoy it!

Margaret Hughes

CAN YOU ANSWER . . . ?

1. Where is the last thatched cottage in Anglesey?

2. Who was One-Leg?

3. How is Penmynydd associated with royalty?

4. What was the baulking system at Amlwch?

5. Anglesey has one square-built lighthouse. Where?

6. This is one of only three churches in Wales dedicated to Saint Patrick . . . where is it and what is its story?

7. Where was the alternative Anglesey harbour for the Irish packet ships during the days of sail?

8. Llyn Alaw – natural or man-made?

9. Newborough once had an industry – what was it?

10. Which Anglesey tradition combines eggs with rice pudding?

11. Where was the Anglesey coalfield?

12. Where is the home of the W.I. movement?

13. How would you pickle a puffin?

14. Two churches on two islands off the Anglesey coast – where are they?

15. What was found at Llyn Cerrig Bach?

16. Where do lions guard an entry?

17. *Who wrote two novels based on Beaumaris?*

18. *Why 'Valley'?*

19. *Where in Anglesey will you find the West Indies?*

20. *Who was Anglesey's most famous artist?*

21. *Where were the Anglesey signal stations?*

22. *This stained glass window depicts Christ as a gardener, wearing a hat. In which church?*

23. *Who was the architect of Beaumaris Castle?*

24. *What is the connection between Holy Island and the Emperor Napoleon?*

25. *What was sold for £444,984.11s.2d in 1841?*

26. *Which well-known author visited Anglesey to search for the birthplace of the poet, Goronwy Owen?*

27. *What does Paymaster Dutton's diary tell us?*

28. *Who were the 'copar-ledis'?*

29. *What is unique about the Menai Strait tides?*

30. *Who was 'the modest millionaire'?*

31. *Anglesey has two airfields; R.A.F. Valley is the more well-known. Where is the other?*

32. *Two tragic accidents happened on an Anglesey railway line – where and when?*

33. *Why is Gallows Point well named?*

34. *Where is the theatre in a barn?*

35. *Were the ferry services to and from Anglesey always 'plane sailing'?*

36. *Why is Cemlyn important ornithologically?*

37. *Divination by water was a superstition at Llanddwyn. How was it claimed to work, and to what end?*

38. *What are the Welsh names for:*
> *The Menai Suspension bridge*
> *Menai Bridge town*
> *Holy Island*
> *Holyhead*
> *Holyhead Mountain*
> *Red Wharf Bay*
> *South Stack*
> *Bull Bay*
> *The Skerries*
> *Point Lynas*
> *Church Island, Menai Bridge*
> *Four Mile Bridge*
> *Puffin Island*

39. *Where will you find a disused brickworks, notable for its inaccessibility?*

40. *Which bird gave the English name to this island?*

41. *What connection does the house at Bodedern named Presaeddfed have with 18th/19th century Bath?*

42. *What route did the old post road take across Anglesey?*

43. What were the industries at Beaumaris during and after the Second World War?

44. 'The Giantess's Apronful' keeps her secret – where?

45. This is the only church in Wales, still holding services, which is lit entirely by candles. Where is it?

46. What would you expect to find at Mariandyrys?

47. What part did Captain William Hutchinson play in the development of Point Lynas?

48. Why are the Bulkeley diaries so important?

49. What does the large stone arch at Holyhead harbour commemorate?

50 There are five blue slate gravestones in Llandegfan church-yard, bearing an anchor and the names of children. What is their story?

51. Where is 'Bedd Branwen' (Branwen's Grave) – who was she?

52. Where would you go to find 'Hendai'?

53. Who was Frances Williams?

54. Oriel Ynys Môn was originally intended as a showcase for which artist's work?

55. Where is Eglwys y Bedd? For what was it once used?

56. Two shipwrecks happened at the same place in Liverpool Bay, exactly one hundred years apart. Where, and which ships?

57. In which Anglesey industry was a kibble used? What was it?

58. Which Anglesey village was associated with witchcraft?

59. What is harvested from the Menai Strait?

60. In which room at Plas Newydd would you find the artist's self-portrait? Who was he?

61. Who was Anglesey's famous Shakespearean actor?

62. How was Telford's Holyhead Road maintained?

63. He lost an arm and his right eye. Holyhead friends erected a memorial to him. Who was he?

64. Where are there traces of the rule of the Welsh Princes?

65. This is a specialised geological centre, open to the public. Where is it?

66. Which lighthouse welcomes the public?

67. Which Anglesey church is famous for its woodcarving?

68. What began with a chicken's broken leg?

69. Who were the Crigyll Robbers?

70. What is unique about Nant y Pandy?

71. Who were the first to walk across the Menai Strait?

72. Where can you see a few items saved from the wreck of 'Royal Charter'?

73. Where is Anglesey's only known motte and bailey castle?

74. *There is a polished granite memorial in a Holy Island churchyard in memory of five men. Who were they? Where is it?*

75. *Where is there a Grade II listed building resembling an upturned boat hull?*

76. *Who was the famous Welsh composer who lived at Menai Bridge?*

77. *Where was an old hulk used to help dam the tide?*

78. *Where could you once enjoy a whitebait tea?*

79. *Who was the self-styled Bishop of Anglesey?*

80. *Which treasured maritime documents came to Anglesey as a result of a recent auction at Sotheby's?*

81. *Which royal yacht sank near the Skerries, and when?*

82. *School slates and slate pencils were made here. Where?*

83. *What is the story of Ellin's Tower?*

84. *She's a working ship with a royal name – where might you see her?*

85. *This was described by a newspaper of 1846 as being used 'by connoisseurs throughout the three kingdoms'. To which product did this refer?*

86. *Where will you see an early burial site, the remains of a medieval chapel and a substantial hut group close together?*

87. *Why is Anglesey favoured by walkers?*

88. *This garden near Cemaes is open to the public once a year. What is its name?*

89. *This is a building on a beach, looking out across a bay. Where is it? What is it?*

90. *Who were the two sisters who became famous for their botanical illustrations?*

91. *Where are Anglesey's 'mountains'?*

92. *Where will you find a stately home for pigeons?*

93. *Who was the Copper King?*

94. *Where are there two ten-foot high standing stones?*

95. *These two lighthouses stand not far from each other.*

96. *There were once many of these on Anglesey. Now only this one works. What? Where?*

97. *He's sculpted in bronze, looking out to sea. Who was he?*

98. *Where would you pick oakum?*

99. *She gave Liberal service to Anglesey. Who was she?*

100. *Which one-time convent chapel has been converted into a successful community centre?*

ANSWERS TO QUIZ QUESTIONS

1. Where is the last thatched cottage in Anglesey?

'Swtan', the last thatched cottage in Anglesey, has been restored and is now a heritage site where visitors can learn about cottage life as it was in days gone by.

A group of local enthusiasts in the Church Bay area prepared a feasibility study of the history of this old cottage which was threatened with demolition. The National Trust, who also had an interest, was concerned about its future during the 1990s, as it was falling into serious decay. Research was done, old deeds were discovered relating to the sale of the property in 1688. Experts agreed that restoration of the cottage could be done to show how it was occupied at the turn of the 20th century, with the help of the last tenants, who were still alive before it was abandoned.

After problems regarding grants were overcome, work began. The thatch was renewed with wheat straw laid on gorse on willow laths. While this was being done an archaeologist undertook a dig on the floor of the cottage, and unearthed several finds which are now shown in the refurbished building.

Visitors from all over the world now call at 'Swtan' to see how an Anglesey farming family lived in the early 1900s. There is an exhibition of women's work – cooking, cleaning, washing, rug making, and a display of farm implements and domestic appliances in the outhouse.

Summertime opening gives those walking the coastal path an opportunity for a break. Other visitors arrive by car, using the local car park so conveniently placed next to the cottage.

How do you find 'Swtan'? Take the Rhydwyn and Church Bay signs off the A5025. Brown signs then lead you the short distance to the car park.

2. Who was One-Leg?

The Anglesey Column, topped by the elegant statue of the first Marquess of Anglesey, gives the answer as he is depicted so, leaning on his stick.

Field Marshall Henry William Paget, Earl of Uxbridge, born in 1768, entered Parliament when only twenty-two years old, and at twenty-five raised a regiment of foot soldiers. Three years later he took command as Lieut. Colonel of the 7th Light Dragoons, a cavalry unit with whom he saw action in the Netherlands and Portugal.

He was a brilliant soldier who eventually became second in command to Wellington. As he was riding with his superior officer from the battlefield of Waterloo his leg was smashed by grapeshot. The story is well-known of how he looked down at his shattered limb and commented 'By God, Sir, I've lost my leg!' to which Wellington is said to have replied equally laconically, 'By God, Sir, so you have!'

His stubborn bravery was put to the test as his leg was amputated, but he recovered sufficiently to return to England three weeks later.

One of the articulated legs made for the 1st Marquess is on show at Plas Newydd. It was so successful that the design for the prosthesis was still being produced, and advertised as 'The Anglesey Leg' until the beginning of the First World War.

3. How is Penmynydd associated with royalty?

The Tudor dynasty was founded when Henry VII became king in 1485. Ednyfed Fychan, who died in 1367, was descended from an ancient Welsh family who owned land in the Penmynydd area of Anglesey. He had served Llywelyn Fawr the Welsh Prince, and had been rewarded for his service with land. Ednyfed's son, Owain Tudor, married king Henry V's widow. Their grandson, Henry, spent fourteen years in exile in Brittany before raising an army, landing on the coast of west Wales to march into England to claim the English throne.

His army and that of king Richard III met at Bosworth Field where Richard was killed in battle, and Henry Tudor succeeded to the throne.

There are associations with the Tudors to be seen in Penmynydd church. Early members of the family are buried in an alabaster tomb, and heraldic devices decorate the interior of the church. An attractive small stained glass window depicts the crown surmounting crossed swords, above the red rose of Lancaster.

The present house at Penmynydd was built in the 17th century on the site of the ancestral Tudor home. It remains in private hands and is not open to the public.

Penmynydd is the village 5km (3 miles) from Menai Bridge on the B5420 Llangefni road from Four Crosses. The church stands apart from the village, approached by either of two lanes which are signposted.

4. What was the baulking system at Amlwch Port?

Facing the open sea in a northerly direction, Amlwch Port, a narrow harbour once busy with small sailing ships, is subjected to what were once called 'dangerous runs' of water, which could swamp shipping and cause extensive damage to vessels and the harbour itself during northerly gales.

The harbour master was permitted to ask captains of ships using the port to order their men to haul heavy baulks of timber across the entrance, one above the other, to provide a breakwater.

In 1851 a byelaw of the Port read . . .

'The Master of a vessel that may be in the Harbour must attend with at least two thirds of his ship's crew to assist in putting down and taking up the Balks (sic) at all times at the call of the Harbour Master or one of the Hobblers, and in case the Master and said portion of his crew be absent or refuse to comply, then the Harbour Master is empowered to engage extra hands for the purpose, and charge the cost thereof on every such vessel and its Master or Owner in proportion to the deficiency.'

Hobblers were responsible for moving vessels in and out of port.

Twenty-three years later a rider was added . . .

'If any Master commits a breach of this byelaw he shall be liable to a penalty not exceeding forty shillings, and also to the cost of any men whom the Harbour Master may employ for the purpose aforesaid.'

This fine was withdrawn in 1918.

There was a warning light which shone when the baulks were in position.

The baulks have gone long since, but the winches used to pull them across the port entrance still survive.

5. *Anglesey has one square-built lighthouse – where?*

Holyhead Breakwater lighthouse was built as part of the long breakwater which was completed in 1873. Clerk of Works at the time was John Hawkshaw, a practical man who realised the difficulty of furnishing a circular room so his answer was obvious, to build a lighthouse designed square to make for easier furnishing. It stands at the end of the long breakwater which snakes out to sea to enclose the New Harbour. The lighthouse is 19.2m high, conspicuous with its black and white striped exterior which makes it easily seen some miles away. The modern light of three flashes every ten seconds can be seen fourteen miles out at sea in clear weather. As are all lighthouses today, the light is automatic.

It is some years since a lighthouseman's family occupied the square rooms. There are plans afoot to convert them into part of the Holyhead Maritime Museum included in the Breakwater Regeneration Plan, when visitors will either walk along to it or be conveyed in a breakwater train.

6. This is one of only three churches in Wales dedicated to Saint Patrick – where is it and what is its story?

Llanbadrig church, north east of Cemaes, is probably the only one of the three which has a direct link with Saint Patrick, the patron saint of Ireland. The site of this Anglesey church dates back to the fifth century and maybe even earlier. Local legend has it that Patrick was shipwrecked on the small island off shore, now called Ynys Badrig, but he succeeded in reaching dry land where he found a cave close by which had a spring. Here he rested to recover, and later built his cell in thanks for his safe landfall.

Throughout the centuries there has been a church here on the cliff top. The original would have been wooden. The earliest date that can be attributed to a stone building at Llanbadrig is the 12th century. There have been many changes over the years and the church was enlarged to its present size during the 15th or 16th centuries.

Today Llanbadrig church has much to interest the visitor. During the restoration of 1884 Henry, 3rd Lord Stanley of Alderley, financed the work on the condition that the decor should show some elements of the Moslem faith as he had converted while in the East. This accounts for the colours of red, blue and white in the windows, the blue glass in the east window, and the blue tiles around the sanctuary.

Geologists marvel at the ICHTHEUS stone which university researchers have proved to be four hundred million years old. They say it was probably hewn in Anglesey about eleven thousand years ago and erected as a standing stone in the neighbourhood in prehistoric times. Early Christian symbols were carved into it between seven and eleven A.D.

Llanbadrig church is a treasure house of geology and ecclesiastical art, in spite of a disastrous fire following expensive restoration in 1985, thought to have been carried out by vandals. But intrepid parishioners raised more money and put the church to rights once more.

7. *Where was the alternative Anglesey harbour for the Irish packet ships during the days of sail?*

Shelter for sailing ships was an important factor in the early 19th century. Holyhead was not always a safe haven – one fact which resulted in the development of the harbour there between 1810 and 1825. When winds veered to an unfavourable direction another shelter had to be found for the sailing packets. A rocky cove to the south of Holy Island provided the answer, and a road was built from Four Mile Bridge for a stage coach to approach. The end of this route led down to the cove and continued along a ledge cut in to the cliff. From here travellers had to finish their approach by climbing down steep steps cut into the rock to a shelter on a flat rocky area to where the ship was moored.

The approach road in its latter stages was narrow, so a coach-and-four would need to be converted to a coach-and-two, both horses in line.

Local people called the cove Porth Dafarch, a corruption of Porth Dau Farch (the port of two horses). The name remains to remind us of this period in the story of the Irish ferries. Today there is little visible evidence of its use. Porth Dafarch was only used in this way for a couple of years because steam packet ships came into use which were not as vulnerable in poor weather as were the sailing ships.

8. Llyn Alaw – natural or man-made?

Anglesey has its natural lakes, set like jewels in the green fields, but Llyn Alaw, between Trefor and Rhosgoch, is not one of those. Until 1988 the shallow Alaw valley was a marsh. Cors y Bol was well suited to become a useful source of water to Anglesey at a time of its greatest need.

When war raged in the 1940s only 16,350 of the population of the island were adequately supplied with water. When evacuees and troops arrived in numbers the water supply system was totally inadequate, a fact which made everyone realise that something had to be done to improve matters if Anglesey was to have successful development after the war ended. The answer came in the form of two reservoirs, the Cefni and the Alaw.

Flooding the marshy Alaw valley brought other compensations, such as allowing the reservoir to become one of Wales's most productive trout fisheries, and an important site for wildfowl and waders. Although not formally a nature reserve, Llyn Alaw is an important winter refuge for wildfowl and summer breeding areas remain relatively undisturbed. There is a small common tern colony at the reservoir, the only inland colony in Wales. Trout fishing is popular, as the quality of the fish is exceptional, well appreciated by anglers who fish along its banks.

The lake is three miles (4.8km) long and a mile wide (1.8km) at its widest point. It covers a surface area of 310 hectares. The average depth is 8ft (2.43m).

There are two approaches to Llyn Alaw, one from Llantrisant and the other from Amlwch and Rhosgoch. The visitor centre at the Llantrisant end of the lake houses an exhibition telling the story of the flooding of the Alaw valley, and there is information on what to see on a visit for bird watchers and nature lovers. The Ranger has an office here. He is often on hand to answer enquiries about fishing permits and sailing.

9. Newborough once had an industry – what was it?

The sand dunes of Newborough, since the time of Elizabeth I, have been the growing ground for marram grass which was first planted to keep the movement of sand in check. The long leaves of this tough grass could be plaited to make a number of useful items, such as mats to cover haystacks, baskets, ropes, nets for rabbit trapping, and brooms.

At one time the Newborough area was a desolate place. There was much poverty, and any means of alleviating this was eagerly grasped. A cottage industry grew up where women were involved.

Marram grass was harvested in the late summer – the plant was respected for its importance in stabilising the dunes. The leaves were left to dry in the air, stacked like sheaves of corn. They gradually changed colour to a rich gold. Then they were carted to homes, ready for plaiting by the women.

For mats, the leaves would be plaited in strips eight metres long, then eight were sewn together. A piece wide enough to cover a haystack would be achieved by sewing several of the strips together to provide a covering measuring eight metres wide.

Bartering was an early method of disposing of the goods. Local shopkeepers would give food in exchange for mats, then take them to market to sell on to farmers.

It was not until the 20th century that any organised form of marketing was introduced to the industry. This came about through the instigation of Col. Stapleton-Cotton, who had organised several country industries in south Anglesey to help the local economy. The Newborough Mat Makers Association put the mat making industry on a firmer footing. The barter system came to an end, and the mat makers had a fairer return for their labour.

By the 20th century rural crafts were in decline. Today only one lady in Newborough is able to work at the craft of marram grass matting.

10. Which Anglesey tradition combines eggs with rice pudding?

A tradition long since disappeared was that of 'Clapio Wyau' (Egg Clapping). This took place before Easter, when groups of children carrying baskets lined with straw would walk around the parish, begging for eggs. They drew attention to themselves by 'clapping' a wooden rattle held in the hand.

A Llansadwrn schoolmaster explained poor attendance to the school inspector by describing the tradition. Reading between the lines one feels he had every sympathy with the children's absence from school on this special occasion.

'March 23, 1891 . . .

'This being the week preceding Easter, there is a marked diminution in the average attendance on account of a custom which seems to be very prevalent here at this time of the year, viz., that of going about the parish in search of eggs which will be devoured to celebrate Easter Holiday. The children that go about carry with them a wooden instrument and a small basket with a small amount of straw at the bottom. This instrument is shaken by the hand, thus producing what they call a 'clap' and from this custom came to be called 'Clapio Wyau Pasg'. The children stand outside the doors of the houses they visit and begin to clap, and when the inmates of the house hear this strange noise they march to the door and present the egg-gatherers with a couple or more – according to the liberality of the farmer – of eggs which the young one deposits safely in his basket. It seems that this collection of eggs is deposited into a magnificent rice pudding prepared especially for the occasion and which is eaten with avidity by the inmates of each house. This being so, it was no wonder that so many children absented themselves from school this week in order to conform with this ancient custom. By means of force and persuasion, I managed to keep the attendance above thirty.'

A week later he wrote in the school log book . . .

'The average attendance for this week is only slightly above last week, and to give a reason for this is too difficult a task for me unless the Easter rice pudding has not agreed with its admirers.'

11. Where was the Anglesey coalfield?

Seams of coal lie in two narrow bands on either side of the Malltraeth marsh.

In 1532 Henry VIII licensed the township of Ysceifiog to exploit it. Some sixty years later Sir Henry Bagnall and Owen Holland agreed to share the rights.

Owen was succeeded by Sir Thomas Holland who maintained his shares until they passed to the Pagets of Plas Newydd. Later, into the 20th century, others were to attempt mining the coalfield but flooding was a constant danger. Spoil heaps were visible along the line of the railway from Pentre Berw to Amlwch.

Production was never extensive, as technical difficulties,

the geological nature of the seams and of the land under which they ran, all made working impossible.

All that is visible today is a chimney to the west of the A5 road at Pentre Berw. The mining ventures of the various families were never wholly successful.

12. Where is the home of the W.I. movement?

Coaches bringing tourists to Llanfair Pwllgwyngyll stop briefly outside the low grey building next to the toll house, for passengers to read the message on a board fixed to the wall. This tells of the founding of the W.I. movement in the village in 1915.

Originally the branch met in a summer house in the garden of 'Graig', a large house up the steep hill opposite, where a number of influential women in Llanfair Pwllgwyngyll first met to hear a Canadian lady, Mrs Watt, describe how the movement had begun in her country to underline the importance of the contribution women were able to make to the economy and, at the same time, enhance their status in the community.

The Canadian W.I. had come to the notice of Col. Stapleton-Cotton, who lived at 'Llwyn Onn', a house on the Plas Newydd estate. He was retired from the army after being severely disabled. He lived his life thereafter in a wheel-chair, but in spite of his disability was active in several agricultural spheres. He believed an organisation such as the W.I. could be popular among women, and also contribute greatly to the life of a country community. So he invited Mrs Watt to speak to an open meeting at 'Graig'. The first branch of the W.I. in Britain was founded there on September 11th, 1915.

In April 1919 it was decided to build a hall for the branch

24

as, by then, its popularity had gained momentum. The site was the gift of the Marquess of Anglesey, adjacent to the toll house. By October 1919 there was £775 in the building fund. Those attending the meeting on December 3rd, 1920, heard that an ex-army hut at the Kinmel Bay camp had been bought and would be erected in Llanfair Pwllgwyngyll. The last meeting at 'Graig' was held in April 1921. The summer house has since been demolished.

The 'new' hall is still the local W.I. meeting room and also the Anglesey Federation office. There are now two institutes in the village, one meeting monthly in the afternoon and the other in the evening.

13. *How would you pickle a puffin?*

The recipe book of Margaret Wynne of Boderwyd gives the following instruction . . .

'Make ye puffins cleane as soon as you take ym & draw ym, yn let ym lie in water & salt a whole night. To wash ym clean in yr liquor and turn up there leggs and parboyle ym in water and salt for halfe an houre and as take ym out of ye hott water shake ym in cold water, and sett ym endwaise to run all night. Next morning lay them flat on there breast in a dry cloth and crush them a little till they be thoroughly dry, yn scrape ym clean with a knife and lay ym on there breasts in a vessell then take a bottle of white wine and as much white wine venegar and a pottle of Alagar, mace, ginger and pepers, yn mace and peper must be brused, ye ginger sliced, yn boyle all these a little in yr liquor with a handful of salt and when it is thoroughly cold cleare it and take ye spice yt is in ye bottom and throw between every lay of ye puffins in ye vessell as you pack ym up poure in ye liquor and putt a round slate or board to keep ym under water and stop ye vessel close yt no wind gett in. This liquor and spice is a fitt proportion for six dozen.'

14. *Two churches on two islands off the Anglesey coast – where are they?*

The date 630 A.D. is carved above the door to the tiny church of Llantysilio, standing on its island below the Menai Suspension bridge. The building itself dates from the 15th century but the foundation of a religious site there goes back to the 7th century as the date suggests. It is cool and dim inside, with simple furnishings as suited to a place of such antiquity.

When the early saints came to Britain they founded cells close to their landing places, some of them on islands where they could be certain of tranquillity and seclusion for the life of meditation and prayer they sought.

Saint Tysilio was said to be the son of Brochfael, Prince of Powys. Other ancient churches in south and west Wales also bear his name which suggests he travelled in those parts, too.

Off the west coast of Anglesey, near to Aberffraw, lies a tiny humped island with a church on top within a high wall. This is at Porth Cwyfan. The church is known as Llangwyfan. Cwyfan was another who sought solitude for his life of contemplation and prayer. Llangwyfan is one of the earliest religious sites in Wales.

The present church dates back to the 11th century. A causeway leads to the island which was used by worshippers in suitable weather, although storms sometimes made access impossible. Plas Llangwyfan nearby had one room which was consecrated and used for services when the causeway was impassable.

The church was repaired in 1893. Occasional services are held there during the summer months.

Time was when a visiting parson was given 'hay for his horse, two eggs for his breakfast and a penny loaf and half a pint of small beer' from a local farm, for holding a service in Llangwyfan church.

The church is often referred to as 'the church in the sea'.

15. What was found at Llyn Cerrig Bach?

The year was 1943. The Royal Air Force station at Valley was being built and the ground prepared for a runway. There were a number of small bogs around the site from which the peat was lifted to cover a layer of sand before the final surface was added. Peat was dragged to the edge of the bogs with a huge wire scoop, then left to dry for a few days. A lorry took the mass to the station and it was spread over the sand with a narrow shovel. While doing this some metal objects and bones came to the surface. Workers knew the source of the peat, a small bog close to Llyn Cerrig Bach. The first object to be found was a gang chain, later to be dated 1900 years old. This prompted a careful search for more.

The engineer in charge recognised the possible importance of the find and sent drawings to the National Museum at Cardiff where experts confirmed that the hoard was one of the most important Iron Age finds to come to light in Britain. More searches were made, more items were found.

At the time it was claimed that still more could be buried at lower levels in the peat, but the need for an Air Force station was paramount at the time so the runway was completed and any further treasure is sealed below the tarmac.

A commemorative stone has been placed by the Anglesey Antiquarian Society to mark the site at the side of one of the perimeter roads around the airfield at Llyn Cerrig Bach.

The total find was considerable. One hundred and forty four objects in all, some large, some small, including weapons and chariot fittings, harness, gang chains used on captive prisoners, shields with decorated bosses, cauldrons, even a trumpet. All were dredged up from the peat by the harrow.

One can only surmise the reason for burying such a hoard. One theory put forward is that the Celts were in the habit of burying their spoils of war in a sacred pool. Can this be why so much treasure was found in one place?

There may be much more buried under the runway at Valley. We shall never know. Most of the items found at Llyn Cerrig Bach are in safe keeping at the National Museum of Wales in Cardiff. One or two are here in Anglesey, at Oriel Ynys Môn.

16. Where do lions guard an entry?

Newcomers visiting Anglesey may have noticed the stone lions at both ends of the Britannia Bridge, now partly hidden by the road deck but once very prominent in the original design when they guarded the rail tracks before they entered and emerged from the tubes. These were designed and executed by John Thomas, a Gloucestershire orphan who went to work for his architect brother in Birmingham, and learnt his trade there. Sir Charles Barry was so impressed by his work that he engaged John Thomas to supervise the stone carving in the then new House of Commons. Thomas was also responsible for the statues on the north and south fronts, the panels bearing the arms of the kings and queens of England from William the Conqueror to Queen Victoria and the bosses in Saint Stephen's Hall.

The stone lions on the Britannia Bridge are each 25ft long and weigh 80 tons. They were made in 1848.

Throughout his comparatively short life of 49 years he completed an enormous amount of work throughout the country, one of his proudest commissions being one from Prince Albert to execute two large reliefs of Peace and War for Buckingham Palace.

17. Who wrote two novels based on Beaumaris?

Joseph Sheridan Le Fanu wrote 'The Tenants of Mallory' and 'Willing to Die'. Both are loosely connected with Beaumaris although he referred to the town as 'Cardyllian'.

Le Fanu was a prolific writer, very popular in his day. The two books mentioned reflect his knowledge of south Anglesey and leave one in no doubt as to the part of the island in which his stories are set. Although Beaumaris becomes Cardyllian, he used the names of the streets as we know them today.

Buildings were referred to by other names, but are recognisable to anyone knowing the town. The Bulkeley Arms became The Vernon Arms, the court house and castle and the pier are all mentioned. The mansion of 'Mallory' was Fryars, then a private home. The Yacht Club receives a mention, as does the George Inn.

Both novels were written only a short while before the author's death. He ended 'The Tenants of Mallory' . . . 'So for the present the story of Verneys of Mallory is told. Years hence, when we shall not be here to read it, the same scenes and family may have a new story to tell, for time with his shuttle and the threads of fate are ever weaving new romance.'

Maybe a future author will take up those threads.

18. Why 'Valley'?

Why, indeed? Ground around the village would appear to be flat, with not a hill in sight.

Experts have been at work trying to trace the origin of the name which first appeared on official documents in 1825 when inns in the parish of Llanynghenedl were applying for licences.

The most likely reason for the name is found in the history of the building of Telford's Holyhead Road. Before the new road existed, the way to Holyhead was across Four Mile Bridge through what is now Trearddur and so to Kingsland and down into the port. Telford planned a new, more direct route, across a cob which he would build over the water from Tŷ Coch, Glasinwen, to his toll house at Penrhos.

This cob, called the Stanley Embankment after the prestigious Stanley family of Penrhos, was a massive undertaking. Completed between 1822 and 1823 it was 1300 yards long, 16ft high, 114ft wide at the base tapering to 14ft at road level. This prompted new building and the hamlet at the Tŷ Coch end came to be known as 'The Valley' as it was from here that much of the earth was removed to be carted to build the embankment.

Today some Welsh residents may prefer the translation 'Dyffryn', but others use the Welsh soubriquet 'Y Fali'.

19. Where in Anglesey will you find the West Indies?

Visitors to Plas Newydd, the home of the 7th Marquess of Anglesey at Llanedwen now belonging to the National Trust, approach the house and grounds through the old dairy and walk down a well defined path alongside a wood. Then the vista opens out to a wide stretch of lawn, interspersed with handsome trees and large beds of shrubs which take on a magical aspect in spring.

This is the main part of the informal garden to the south of the house, above the small harbour. There are massed hydrangeas and camellias, some as old as pre 1914, huge beds of deciduous azaleas and Japanese maples, some cedars, flowering cherries and magnolias. In spring this garden comes into its own.

A tree house perched in the branches of one of the larger trees on the estate was a playground for the more adventurous young members of the family in days gone by.

The latest addition is a bed of summer flowering azaleas, planted some ten years ago in memory of a one-time volunteer steward for the National Trust, who spent many hours here. This is beneath the trees at the upper end of the garden, and brings a welcome splash of colour to what was previously a more sombre spot.

This informal garden is called 'The West Indies', a name which must have been given many, many years ago, as nobody today knows the reason why. But it is a name still used.

20. Who was Anglesey's most famous artist?

Sir Kyffin Williams R.A. died in 2006 and was buried in the churchyard at Llanfair-yng-Nghornwy. He was born outside Llangefni in 1918 and had his early education in a small preparatory school at Trearddur Bay before going on to Shrewsbury School.

Although accepted and given a commission by the Royal Welsh Fusiliers, he was unable to take it up owing to an attack of epilepsy, so he spent a few years immediately before the Second World War working in a land agent's office in Pwllheli. The family had moved by this time to live in that area. Eventually he was ordered by the War Office to attend a hospital in Oxford for assessment, which proved conclusively that he was indeed epileptic, and, in the doctor's brusque comment, 'abnormal' and of no use to the services. That same doctor made the suggestion which was to give Wales one of its most prestigious painters – 'You should take up art'.

Kyffin Williams was accepted by the Slade School of Art as a student. He later described himself as 'the worst student there'. Nevertheless, at the end of the three years' course he was awarded the Robert Ross Leaving Prize.

For a time he taught art at Highgate School, later working there part-time so that he could spend time to paint in his studio. He did not start to paint seriously until 1947.

Today his distinctive pictures – portraits and landscapes – are much prized. He once said, 'I was lucky I was born into a landscape so beautiful I had no need to go elsewhere.'

Kyffin Williams was knighted during his latter years and among his art associations he appreciated particularly his connection with the Royal Cambrian Society, based at Conwy, for whom he was President. He never married, but lived alone on the shore of his beloved Menai Strait at

Pwllfanog near Llanfair Pwllgwyngyll. His funeral service at
Bangor Cathedral was attended by several hundred mourners.

21. Where were the Anglesey signal stations?

An early warning system set up to allow Liverpool shipowners
and merchants news of the approach of their ships into the
Liverpool port was devised in the early 19th century. This
was when Liverpool's facilities were so much in demand.

The method used was semaphore. A line of stations
stretched from Holyhead to Bidston Hill on the Wirral, the
last one easily discernable from the dockside offices the
other side of the Mersey. This was in operation in 1827.

The Holyhead station was built on Holyhead Mountain
between the summit and South Stack; the next was on a low
hilltop at Carreglwyd near Llanfaethlu. The Cefn Du station
was on the slope of Mynydd y Garn near Llanrhuddlad. The
next, on the side of Mynydd Eilian close to Point Lynas, sent
messages on to the north eastern point of Puffin Island, from
where they were sent across to Llandudno and so on down
the line to Bidston.

Signals were conveyed by means of two tall masts, each
fitted with four arms, each arm operated from a room in the
station house. The alphabet was shown by numbers. The
system worked well in clear weather and the speed of
transmission was remarkable as the men in charge became
expert. It could take less than a minute for messages to
arrive in Liverpool from Holyhead. The published list of
messages with their appropriate numbers still exists.

From 1860 the semaphore system was discontinued as
electrical transmission took its place. The Point Lynas and
Carreglwyd stations were converted, the other buildings
used as private dwellings or allowed to decay.

22. This stained glass window depicts Christ as a gardener, wearing a hat. In which church?

The slim spire of Llanwenllwyfo church, overlooking Dulas, is a pointer to the answer. This building replaced another church, probably medieval, which stood in the grounds of the Llys Dulas estate. This is now a ruin. Degeneration of the fabric led to the need for a replacement which would also meet the needs of a growing congregation.

Bangor architect Henry Kennedy, who was responsible for several new churches in the 19th century, was commissioned. All the cost of £1147 was met by donations, the largest being the gift of Gertrude Dowager Lady Dinorben of Llys Dulas. Another of the Llys Dulas family, young Gwyn Gertrude Hughes, laid the foundation stone in 1854. She was nine years old at the time.

The church was opened for services in 1856. In 1871 Gwyn Gertrude Hughes married Sir Arundell Neave. The marriage was short. He was a collector of object d'art and had among his treasures some precious Flemish stained glass, some of which he presented to St Gwenllwyfo's church at Llanwenllwyfo. This 15th century glass was re-set in seventeen single lights and portions of the others in the head of the east window. This was in 1876, the year before Sir Arundell Neave died.

One of the windows features Christ as the gardener, wearing a hat – one of very few such in Britain.

34

23. Who was the architect of Beaumaris Castle?

Beaumaris Castle was one of Edward I's creations, one of five stupendous fortresses built in north-west Wales to quell any threatened revolt by the warring Welsh. Caernarfon, Conwy, Cricieth and Harlech were the others.

Edward commissioned James St George, an architect from Savoy, in 1295. He planned and put into work what is now regarded as the most perfect concentric fortress design. Four hundred masons, two thousand labourers, thirty smiths and carpenters, worked on a site on the seashore. In three years building had reached the stage when the castle could be defended. After that the pace of work decreased over the next twenty-five years. Beaumaris Castle was never completed.

Some fighting took place during the uprising of Owain Glyndŵr, and it was held in a state of defence at the time of the Civil War but no fighting happened there then.

Now the sea has receded and only the moat washes the castle walls. When Edward I chose the site, the town of Llanfaes nearby bustled with activity. But gradually this was replaced in importance as the new town grew around the castle and attracted commerce. Some of the inhabitants of Llanfaes were moved to set up a new village in the south-western corner of the island which was then named Newborough.

24. What is the connection between Holy Island and the Emperor Napoleon?

Napoleon's prison accommodation on St Helena was a 56-roomed bungalow built by the British government. Its opulent furnishings included a large table made of green marble, quarried on Holy Island. This attractive stone which Thomas Pennant described as being 'green, black and a dull purple' polished to a richly coloured surface. The table must have been particularly handsome.

It was made by George Bullock, a furniture maker highly praised in the same category as Chippendale. It is said that Bullock gained control of the Bodior quarry and others in Anglesey wherever the stone came to the surface. There are examples of furniture and furnishings incorporating this unusual stone elsewhere in the country. There is one in Anglesey, where a chimney piece at Plas Rhianfa on the Menai Bridge to Beaumaris road has inset panels of the so-called 'Green Marble'.

George Bullock died at the early age of thirty-five.

The Bodior quarry stands by the side of the road from Four Mile Bridge to Rhoscolyn shortly after crossing the inland Sea. All is quiet there now, except for the occasional amateur geologist on the lookout for a specimen.

Mona Marble, as it was also called in commercial circles, was quarried in several parts of Anglesey. Experts rated it highly as 'verd antique' and compared it favourably with Italian marble.

25. What was sold for £444,984.11s.2d in 1841?

There had been a warning light on The Skerries, off the treacherous north coast of Anglesey, since 1716. At first it was an open fire in a brazier placed on the top of a round stone tower, for which the owner was allowed to charge passing ships light dues. The fuel used was coal – between eighty and a hundred tons a year.

Ownership passed down one family over the years. In 1778 the brazier gave way to a lantern with reflectors which enlarged the light of an oil lamp placed inside it. This was a great improvement, as before the light from the fire had often been obscured by smoke.

In 1835 Trinity House offered to buy the rocky islands. By this time the shipping lanes across Liverpool Bay were busy with vessels using the port of Liverpool, and greater development was a possibility. The owner of the light was making a tidy fortune of nearly £2000 a year from light dues and these, too, promised to increase as time passed. So the offer to buy was refused. Trinity House made another offer and this, too, was turned down as was yet another, of £360,000 three years later.

In 1841 the question of ownership was settled by a special jury sitting at the Sheriff's Court in Beaumaris, when the final sum of £444,984.11s.2d was fixed. The islands then became the property of Trinity House and the last remaining lighthouse then in private hands on the coast of Britain became theirs. The ancillary buildings on the islands have recently been restored. The light is operated automatically from the Trinity House headquarters at Harwich.

26. Which well-known author visited Anglesey to search for the birthplace of the poet, Goronwy Owen?

George Borrow, his wife and daughter, undertook a long tour of Wales in 1854. One of the purposes was to visit Anglesey to search for the birthplace of one of Borrow's favourite Welsh poets, Goronwy Owen.

Borrow's knowledge of the Welsh language was a source of great pride to him, and he used it wherever he could on his travels.

Leaving his wife and daughter to make their way back to Llangollen from Bangor by train, he crossed the Menai Suspension bridge into Anglesey and began his search, walking along the Pentraeth road. Borrow talked to anyone and everyone, and met some interesting characters who he described vividly in his book, *Wild Wales*. There was Mr Pritchard, the innkeeper of The White Horse at Pentraeth, the children at Llanfair Mathafarn Eithaf, the miller and his wife who gave him tea, bread and butter and watery cheese and honoured him with lump sugar in his tea, and the old woman who lived at Tŷ Gronwy. All combined to make a never-to-be-forgotten memory of Anglesey in the mid 19th century for today's readers.

27. What does Paymaster Dutton's diary tell us?

An Irish ferry boat previously called *Hibernia* which was converted for patrol service during the First World War was re-named *Tara*. After a period patrolling the Irish sea she was ordered to the Mediterranean. Paymaster Alfred Dutton was one of her crew. He was a Holyhead man, as were most of the crew. They left port and sailed for the Middle East in 1915. *Tara* cruised along the coast of North Africa where she was torpedoed. Ninety-three of the crew took to the boats which were towed to land at Port Suliman by the Germans.

Four months of suffering followed. Paymaster Dutton recorded the crew's experiences as prisoners of war, describing how they almost starved to death, were made to work in intense heat under harsh conditions with little hope of release. But the morale of the crew was maintained throughout, although almost at breaking point at times.

But freedom did come, very unexpectedly in the form of a motor vehicle cavalcade which crossed the desert to search for them, led by the Duke of Westminster. The cavalcade even included an ambulance. The prisoners were released and taken to Alexandria to recuperate after their ordeal.

Their welcome home to Holyhead, strengthened as they were by rest and diet, was ecstatic. The story of their exploits was common discussion in the town for as long as the crew lived to tell the tale.

The local Maritime Museum has pictures of the official welcome home. Paymaster Dutton's diary is a valued item in the County Record Office collection.

28. Who were the 'copar-ledis'?

When the copper mining industry at Mynydd Parys flourished during the latter years of the 18th and the early 19th centuries the large workforce included a band of women whose duties were to break up the ore into small manageable pieces ready for the smelter, discarding the waste. They worked in purpose built sheds on the mountain, sixty or eighty at a time. Their hours were long, but the work was not arduous, and they were paid more than they would have received had they worked on the farms – tenpence for a twelve-hour shift. When the women became too old to continue they were sometimes given a small pension of eighteen pence a week.

The 'copar-ledi' used an industrial glove on her left hand. This had iron rings around the fingers. With this she would lift a lump of ore, place it on a knock-stone, and with a long-handled, narrow mallet trim the ore of its waste and knock it into smaller sized pieces.

The women wore a dress which was almost a uniform, as they were all dressed alike. This consisted of a petticoat of home spun and woven wool, a yellow shoulder bag and apron, and a kerchief tied crossways under a tall Welsh hat. On Sundays, for church or chapel, they appeared transformed, many of them wearing clothes which their farm worker contemporaries could not afford.

29. What is unique about the Menai Strait tides?

The Menai Strait is 18 miles (29km) long from Penmon in the north-east to Abermenai in the south-west. The width varies, the narrowest point being at Menai Bridge and along to the Britannia bridge. The tide race can be vicious.

Experienced sailors do not take the Menai Strait lightly. It is shallow in places, with outcrops of rock which show themselves at low tide, but there are also deep pools. Currents run swiftly. Woe betide the careless sailor who takes a short cut instead of keeping to the channels marked by buoys. And he must be aware of the unusual pattern of the tides.

Being open at both ends, the Strait has two high and two low tides daily. Flood tide (low to high) water races in through the narrow entrance at Abermenai and similarly from Beaumaris, towards Menai Bridge, and both meet between the two bridges. The flow stops here but water level continues to rise. Then water begins to flow back, in the reverse direction.

Tidal currents can reach eight knots. Great care is needed by every size of craft to negotiate a passage and even minutes' delay can be crucial. This was clearly demonstrated some fifty years ago, when the *Conway*, a school training ship, one-time man o' war, was being moved from her permanent position in the Strait to sail to Liverpool for re-fitting. Very exact timing was necessary for the two tugs to ease her gently from her mooring into the channel and past the notorious Swelly Rocks. As their timing was fractionally incorrect, *Conway* fouled, had to be abandoned, and eventually broke her back.

The Swelly Rocks have a light upon them today as a constant warning to sailors. The light stands proud at high tide when the rocks are submerged.

30. Who was 'the modest millionaire'?

Few had heard of Vivian Hewitt until 1912 when he became the first to fly across the Irish Sea. In later life he lived at 'Bryn Aber', the house on the promontory at Cemlyn on the north coast of Anglesey. He was a recluse, preferring his own company and that of the wildlife as far as possible.

Hewitt came from a wealthy family of brewers in Grimsby. As a young man he was apprenticed as an engineer at the Portsmouth Dockyard then at the Crewe railway works, experience which was to stand him in good stead later in his life. On completing his engineering training he experimented with gliders, powered aircraft, motor cycles and cars, and became a racing driver on the Brooklands circuit. Flying offered a particular attraction to the young Hewitt. He was sufficiently wealthy to be able to buy his own aircraft in which he created a world record by flying seventy-five miles across to Dublin via Holyhead.

During the First World War he worked on aircraft engines in America, but poor health prevented any record attempts so he switched his attention to motor boats and a very different type of flying – ornithology.

Bird watching brought him to Anglesey, where he leased 'Bryn Aber' at Cemlyn with the intention of creating a bird sanctuary. But this was not to be. The Second World War intervened and the land he had chosen was earmarked for agriculture.

After his death in 1965 four furniture vans were needed to move his vast collection of birds' eggs to the headquarters of the British Trust for Ornithology at Tring. Vivian Hewitt was buried in his beloved garden, behind the high wall at 'Bryn Aber'.

31. Anglesey has two airfields; R.A.F. Valley is the more well-known. Where is the other?

Mona airfield, visible from the A5 road between Rhostrehwfa and Gwalchmai, is the older of the two airfields. It was created to be a base for small airships which patrolled the Irish Sea and Liverpool Bay at a time when German U-boats were uncomfortably active during the First World War.

Land was acquired and work began on building the runway and the station buildings, a task considered of great importance and many were employed. In those days it was called Llangefni Airfield. A large shed was built to house four airships. There were the necessary workshops, a gas plant and accommodation for personnel. Airships were used in reconnaissance, to relay details of submarine activity threatening surface vessels sailing in and out of Holyhead and Liverpool. The service operated by the Royal Naval Air Service lasted only a few years, until the end of the war in 1918. By 1920 all was silent at Mona airfield. The site was sold to Anglesey County Council. Today it is used for private flying, but is on call as an emergency airfield if necessary. Part of the land is now a business park.

32. Two tragic accidents happened on an Anglesey railway line – where and when?

Opening in 1864, the Anglesey Central Railway operated services from Gaerwen to Amlwch for nearly one hundred years. During that time there were two accidents. The first occurred in 1877 on a section of the track between Llannerch-y-medd and Amlwch where it ran alongside the Alaw, then crossed the river by a low stone bridge. The November night had been dark and very wet, so wet that a small dam upstream had burst and a body of water rushed into the river, demolishing the bridge.

The first train early the following morning started its journey unaware of the damage, and in the darkness both engine and coaches toppled into the river. Fortunately there was only one passenger, but he and three crew died, three of them being badly burned by steam but did not survive their injuries.

In 1926 the second fatal accident occurred, again on the stretch of track between Llannerch-y-medd and Amlwch when a late evening train ran over an obstacle on the line during a dark night. Next morning two bodies were found, a man and a woman who were workers on a nearby farm. The inquest resulted in an open verdict.

The Gaerwen to Amlwch service ceased during the mid 20th century as a result of the Beeching cuts. Since then efforts have been made to re-open the service, but these, for various reasons, have been unsuccessful.

33. Why is Gallows Point well named?

Sailors who leave their craft high and dry for the winter on the land west of Beaumaris speak of it as Gallows Point. But how many know its story?

Here stood the gallows in the days before 1829, after which all executions took place in the new gaol at Beaumaris. Legend has it that pirates' and smugglers' corpses were left to rot at the Point, as a warning to passing sailors.

Gallows Point shared the dubious honour with the Castle. Executions out of doors gave the local populace the opportunity to witness, and to make a holiday of the occasion.

Sentence of death could be passed for a variety of crimes in those early days, some of which we would regard today as petty.

In 1468 seven brothers were hanged for murder and robbery. In 1593 Catholic priest William Davies received the death penalty for treason. Proven witchcraft was another reason for a hanging. In 1719 seventeen years old Thomas Esay of Beddgelert was sentenced to death for stealing a horse. A woman from Llanddaniel met her end for committing robbery, so did two Irish tinkers who robbed Llantysilio church. An Irish woman found guilty of attempted murder at Bodedern went to the gallows as did men convicted of sheep stealing.

Several of these executions took place at Gallows Point.

34. Where is the theatre in a barn?

In 1949 those interested in amateur dramatics in Llangefni banded together to form a society, under the leadership of George Fisher, a native of Glamorgan who was a mathematics teacher at Llangefni County School. George Fisher was an Englishman who had learned Welsh – self-taught – with such success that he wrote plays in Welsh and won prizes for them at the National Eisteddfod on three occasions.

He was the founder – secretary of the new society. Their first production was a costume play with twenty-five characters, produced on a shoestring but, showing for three nights with full houses there was enough profit to buy a spotlight with the proceeds. Within a short time an ambitious programme of plays, readings, discussions and lectures had been prepared.

Rehearsals and play performances took place in the County School hall. The plays were Welsh and English, some written by George Fisher himself. Members took stage parts, painted scenery, made costumes, took back stage and front of house responsibility. At the end of each rehearsal everything had to be dismantled and stored in a disused swimming pool at the school. By this time the society had four hundred members. There was great enthusiasm and support.

Storage facilities came to an end when the swimming pool building had to be demolished. This prompted enquiries about a permanent home. The Urban District Council was buying the Pencraig estate at the time. The society rented outbuildings there for five shillings a week then bought them from the U.D.C. for £250. Conversion began in 1955 with volunteers doing most of the work.

'Theatr Fach' as it is called, was opened in May 1955

when two plays, one in Welsh and the other in English, were performed.

The society went on to receive a grant from the Gulbenkian Trust towards the cost of improvements to the theatre. As a member of the Little Theatres Guild of Great Britain the society's status in amateur drama was enhanced.

George Fisher died in 1970. A rehearsal room has been built in his memory.

Theatr Fach has produced actors and technicians who have since become household names in radio and television. The company has taken plays to Ireland and America and still attracts regular audiences to its presentations at the little theatre at Pencraig.

35. Were the ferry services to and from Anglesey always 'plane sailing'?

Before the Menai Suspension bridge opened in 1826 the six ferries across the water performed a very necessary service. Some dated back to medieval times.

In the days before Beaumaris overtook Llanfaes in importance a ferry was based at Llanfaes to sail at low tide to meet travellers coming from the mainland on horseback or on foot over the exposed Lavan Sands. This service later moved to Beaumaris. Another, the *Garth* ferry, crossed from Porth Esgob below what is now Upper Bangor to Cadnant near Porthaethwy, a distance of two miles. The *Porthaethwy* boat took the shortest route across the narrowest part of the Strait.

Moel y Don ferry took passengers to Felinheli. Another plied from Tal y Foel to the Bangor side of Caernarfon, and two other boats serviced the Caernarfon passage, one directly to the town from Abermenai and the other, to a point west of the town at Foryd.

All these passages had their problems. Careful navigation was needed, and accidents happened.

In 1664 there was an argument aboard the *Abermenai* boat which turned physical, and the consequent abrupt movement of passengers resulted in the ferry capsizing with a death toll of seventy-nine. In 1710 the *Moel y Don* boat sank with fifteen men and ten horses aboard, but they were all able to reach land as it happened in shallow water.

The *Tal y Foel* boat overturned in 1723, when thirty drowned, but two passengers were saved, one a boy who had the sense to cling to a horse's tail as the animal swam to safety. A woman lived to tell her lucky story after the *Porthaethwy* ferry was overloaded and spilled its passengers into the water. She was one of two survivors, thanks to her voluminous skirts which ballooned and kept her afloat.

Another tragedy occurred in 1785 when fifty-five died as the *Abermenai* boat, which was overloaded with people returning to Anglesey after a day at Caernarfon Fair, sank in a particularly treacherous part of the Strait.

The last ferry service ended during the middle of the twentieth century. By that time the motor car and the train had replaced the old ways of crossing the Menai Strait.

The last thatched cottage – see question 1

A royal hearth – see question 3

A square lighthouse – see question 5

Newborough's traditional industry – see question 9

Home of the W.I. movement – see question 12

An island church – see question 14

Llyn Cerrig Bach – see question 15

Anglesey's most famous artist – see question 20

An Edwardian castle – see question 23

Mynydd Parys – see question 28

Menai Strait – see question 29

Gallows Point, Beaumaris – see question 33

Holyhead – see question 38

Puffin Island – see question 38

A disused brickworks – see question 39

The old Mona Hotel on Telford's Holyhead road – see question 42

Barclodiad y Gawres ('the giantess' apronful') – see question 44

Point Lynas – see question 47

Oriel Ynys Môn – see question 54

Plas Newydd – see question 60

One of Telford's 'sunburst' gates – see question 62

Rhosyr – see question 64

South Stack lighthouse – see question 66

Nant y Pandy, Llangefni – see question 70

Royal Charter memorial – see question 72

An upturned boat – see question 75

Llannerch-y-medd – see question 85

Early hut group – see question 86

Ynys Llanddwyn – see question 87

An Anglesey windmill – see question 88

A Maritime Museum – see question 89

A lifeboat hero – see question 97

36. Why is Cemlyn important ornithologically?

The lagoon at Cemlyn is a breeding area for many birds, but especially important for having the only substantial colony of Sandwich terns in Wales. A large number of Common and Arctic terns also breed here, also a few Roseate terns. When Arctic terns begin to nest on the shingle ridge visitors are asked to be careful where they walk, and to follow signs between green-topped posts. Quietness is essential if the birds are not to be alarmed.

The tern colony is of particular interest when these migrant birds return to Cemlyn to nest and breed in the summer. Arctic terns will have flown from the other side of the world to nest here each year. It is estimated that the bird can live up to twenty years, and during that time will have flown no less than two hundred thousand miles from Britain to Antarctica and back each year.

Other birds breeding at Cemlyn include mallard, shellduck, several warblers, gulls, and plovers. There are also wintering wildfowl and several passage migrants.

When Captain Vivian Hewitt lived at 'Bryn Aber', the walled house and garden at the Point, he managed Cemlyn privately as a wildfowl refuge. It is now leased from the National Trust by the North Wales Wildlife Trust who guard the area carefully as one of their Anglesey nature reserves.

The ridge is storm driven shingle. Some of the pebbles are from the Lake District and Scotland, brought down by ice sheets.

Cemlyn lies on the northern coast, two miles west of the Wylfa Magnox Power Station. It is signposted from the A5025 at Tregele, down lanes leading to two car parks.

37. Divination by water was a superstition at Llanddwyn. How was it claimed to work, and to what end?

Dwynwen, daughter of Brychan, a British chieftain, sought solitude at Llanddwyn after a broken love affair, where she built a cell and later a church was erected on the site. The legend tells how, because she sympathised with others in the same predicament, she infused a well of water with special power. Those who wished to know their fate would visit the well, scatter a few wholemeal breadcrumbs on the surface of the water then cover it lightly with a cloth. An eel would appear, to take the crumbs. If the cloth was disturbed enough to make it sink under the water the woman would know that her lover was faithless. Thankful for the warning, she would place an offering before leaving.

The well is still there . . . but we are not a superstitious race any longer!

There are several wells at Llanddwyn. One has a curious yet suitable name – 'Crochan Llanddwyn' (Llanddwyn cooking pot). Pure spring water is forced to the surface through whirling particles of sand, making it appear to be boiling. Through ignorance of the scientific reason, the phenomenon was steeped in superstition.

38. What are the Welsh names for . . .

The Menai Suspension bridge	Pont y Borth
Menai Bridge town	Porthaethwy
Holy Island	Ynys Cybi
Holyhead	Caergybi
Holyhead Mountain	Mynydd Twr
Red Wharf Bay	Traeth Coch
South Stack	Ynys Lawd
Bull Bay	Porth Llechog
The Skerries	Ynysoedd y Moelrhoniaid
Point Lynas	Trwyn Eilian
Church Island, Menai Bridge	Ynys Tysilio
Four-Mile Bridge	Pontrhydybont
Puffin Island	Ynys Seiriol

39. Where will you find disused brickworks notable for their inaccessibility?

The brickworks at Porth Wen, on the rugged north coast between Cemaes and Bull Bay, was productive during the first quarter of the twentieth century. Bricks of a yellow white colour were made there, a speciality as they would withstand very high temperatures due to the high percentage of silica in the clay.

In 1906 a German bought the works and introduced the method of cutting the bricks into shape with wire. Two years later he was followed by Charles Tidy who expanded the scope of the works and introduced yet another new technique, that of making glazed bricks and tiles by the press method. The works closed in 1914.

The coastal site at Porth Wen was not ideal for such an industry, as road access was almost impossible and everything had to be brought in and taken away from the works by sea. The sea at Porth Wen often carries a heavy swell and ship owners regarded a stay at the quay with trepidation as their vessels were often damaged by striking the seabed or the harbour wall.

40. Which bird gave the English name to this island?

The squat, black and white-plumed birds with bright orange, yellow and blue parrot-like bills are a feature of Ynys Seiriol during the breeding season, giving the island its English name – Puffin Island.

The colony has decreased latterly. A bird count in 1990 revealed only thirty pairs, whereas the same count showed there to be a colony of over four hundred pairs of cormorants and a large number of kittiwakes.

In days gone by, when puffins nested on the island in great numbers, they were caught, pickled and exported in barrels. Trade was good as there were many who considered them a delicacy. They were the subject of a variety of recipes (see question 13) especially in the kitchens of the great houses across the border in England and even abroad.

Mid summer is breeding time. The puffin spends most of the year far out at sea, flying great distances from the nest. The bird is an excellent diver. As its bill has a unique system of razor sharp edges and backward pointing spikes, it can carry fish in quantity without swallowing.

Puffins nest in burrows dug into the ground – this is probably one reason why rats on Ynys Seiriol have been so successful in decimating the puffin population.

Puffins arrive between February and early April. Burrows can be as deep as six feet. Sometimes they take over abandoned rabbit burrows. The same pair can return to the same burrow year after year. The female lays one egg, which takes five or six weeks to hatch, both male and female taking turns to incubate it. They feed the chick for six weeks then abandon it. Hunger makes the chick adventurous and it flies out to sea to learn to fish for itself.

Because of its ungainly movement on land and its distinctive appearance, the puffin has always been regarded with slightly humorous affection. In reality it is a tough little bird with incredible staying power out at sea in the roughest weather.

As well as the activity of rats on the island, fall in numbers is also blamed on fishing problems far away from Britain as puffins find it more difficult to find enough food due to over fishing in the North Sea and elsewhere.

41. What connection does the house named 'Presaeddfed' at Bodedern have with 18th/19th century Bath?

During the 18th century Sir John Bulkeley lived at 'Presaeddfed' with Margaret, his daughter. To the disappointment of the family she married James King, an Irishman of no social standing who worked as Master of Ceremonies at Bath where society flocked to socialise and take the waters. An engraving of handsome James King hangs in one of Bath's public rooms today. He was born in Dublin. He held his position in Bath between 1785 and 1816, and also at Cheltenham as the two seasons did not coincide. The remainder of the year he spent at Bodedern.

Margaret returned to live permanently at 'Presaeddfed' after her husband's death, where James's illegitimate son took great care of her.

42. What route did the old post road take across Anglesey?

So called because it was the route taken by the coaches carrying mail to the port of Holyhead, thence to be shipped to Ireland, the post road crossed Anglesey diagonally. Sometimes mail was brought over the Lavan Sands to Beaumaris; at other times the shorter Bangor to Porthaethwy route was chosen, depending on the weather. Two tracks – they hardly merited the name roads – led from Beaumaris and Porthaethwy town to Ceint, where they met to continue through Llangefni, Gwyndy and Bodedern, to cross over the Inland Sea to Holy Island at Four Mile Bridge and so through Kingsland into Holyhead.

In 1675 cartographer James Ogilby published his ribbon map of the London-Holyhead Post Road, marking the towns and villages and some of the features to be seen from the road.

Travellers who have written of their experiences all mention the atrocious road conditions across Anglesey before Telford's day. Stones and mud, churned up after rain, made the going difficult, especially for a cumbersome coach and four horses.

Jonathan Swift, in 1727, took nearly twelve hours to ride from Porthaethwy to Holyhead. He described the road as being 'ill kept for the first five miles, being pitched with great stones, but suffered to lie in great holes . . . the descent to the ferry house is execrably rough and dirty'.

Gwyndy, the large inn between Llangefni and Bodedern, was regarded as a welcome break from the trials of travel. Here horses could be changed and a meal and accommodation, if necessary, prepared for the weary traveller. Little of Gwyndy remains today, but a rough gable end and one tall chimney marks the spot. When Thomas Telford's new road was opened it took a different route. The improved surface

70

cut journey time considerably and made for more comfortable travel. So Gwyndy lost many of its customers who abandoned the post road and began to travel the new, patronising the Mona Inn beyond Rhostrehwfa, a facility provided by Telford. This, too, is now a shadow of its former self, having been a farmhouse for many years.

43. What were the industries at Beaumaris during and after the Second World War?

The visitor today hardly regards Beaumaris as an industrial area, yet during the Second World War there was much activity at Llanfaes, a mile or so outside the town. Today all is peaceful.

Here a factory which was part of the Hawker Siddeley Group converted and maintained flying boats. The site, a one time Fransiscan Friary, has seen several companies making a variety of products, from radio telescope reflectors to floating pontoons.

After the war, until 1953, the company named Saunders Engineering Shipyard Ltd made bus bodies in great numbers. London Transport was among their best customers, receiving three hundred double-decker buses from the Anglesey factory over a number of years.

In 1946 the world's first aluminium fast patrol boat came off the stocks, also inshore minesweepers, landing craft and pleasure boats were later products.

Over the years mergers were frequent. Saunders Engineering Shipyard Ltd eventually became Saro (Anglesey) Ltd which in turn became Gloster Saro Ltd. That company then merged with Cammell Laird of Birkenhead.

The once busy site is now relatively quiet. The house of

'Fryars' is now privately owned. The birds have returned to the grounds of 'Fryars' and the foreshore, which was such a busy place during the productive years, is now the haunt of seabirds once more.

44. 'The Giantess's Apronful' keeps her secret – where?

How this magnificent ancient tomb received its name, 'Barclodiad y Gawres', is a mystery. It stands high above the sea on the south-west coast of Anglesey, not far from Rhosneigr. A narrow passage leads between the massive stones at the entrance to a spacious central chamber from which branch three smaller chambers. The great stone tomb stands on an earth mound.

There had been some disturbance here before a more careful examination was made by archaeologists during the last century, and only a few cremated bones were found latterly.

Barclodiad y Gawres is famed in archaeological circles for the decorated stones, five of them, which the experts tell us have been marked by using a stone chisel. There are lively scrolls and zigzag line patterns, the kind of abstract art found often in similar tombs in Ireland. Their meaning has never been interpreted satisfactorily. It is guessed that the tomb dates from between 2500 BC and 2400 BC, give or take a century.

Another Barclodiad y Gawres can also be seen in the Conwy valley. A legend there tells of a giantess having shaken free an apronful of stones. Could this legend also be attributed to the Anglesey burial chamber?

45. This is the only church in Wales, still holding services, which is lit entirely by candles. Where is it?

The tall spire of Llanedwen parish church is a landmark for sailors on the Menai Strait. The religious site here is said to have been founded by the Saxon Saint Edwen but the present building is some 150 years old. Gravestones suggest a much earlier foundation, and there are church furnishings and decoration which point to the 18th, 17th and even 15th centuries.

This is the parish church of the Plas Newydd estate, supported regularly by the Marquess and Marchioness of Anglesey from their home nearby. There are family graves and those of retainers in the churchyard.

One of Anglesey's most famous men is buried here, too. He was Henry Rowlands, cleric and antiquary, born at Plas Gwyn, Llanedwen, in 1655. He had charge of five parishes in south Anglesey but found time in a busy life to research and write a study of agriculture on the island during his lifetime. His *Mona Antiqua Restorata* was published. His agricultural researches give us a vivid picture of the state of farming in Anglesey during the 17th/18th centuries.

46. *What would you expect to find at Mariandyrys?*

Mariandyrys is a fifteen-acres site on a small hill close to Glan yr Afon near Llangoed. It is leased and cared for by the North Wales Wildlife Trust as a nature reserve, open to the public, one of several on the island.

The ridge forming the reserve is an outcrop of carboniferous limestone which extends below the sea to Puffin Island and the Orme at Llandudno. It is mostly grassland, covered with heather and gorse, with patches of grassland here and there where rabbits and sheep have been busy. These green patches are the home of many species of wild flowers.

The old quarry, long since disused, features many species of rare plants, a delight to any botanist. Here there are over twenty species of butterflies and eighty species of moths. Snails abound here – ample food for song thrushes who break the snails' shells open on the quarry stones. Jackdaws nest in holes in the rock face. The tawny owl and the brown owl are frequent visitors. Many smaller birds such as linnets, yellowhammers, stonechats, dunnock, sedge warblers, whitethroats, chiff chaff and willow warblers can be seen at Mariandyrys.

Descriptive leaflets of the Trust's reserves on the island are available at Information Centres, some libraries, and from the Trust's office in Bangor High Street.

47. What part did Captain William Hutchinson play in the development of Point Lynas?

Captain William Hutchinson was appointed Liverpool Dockmaster in 1759. The port of Liverpool was expanding rapidly, with ships from countries worldwide beginning to use its facilities. Coastal vessels' captains knew the dangers of Liverpool Bay and the Mersey approaches, but foreign ships' masters did not. There had been some kind of pilotage system in operation, but this was in need of regulating so an Act was passed to this end. The act stipulated charges to be made on ships using the pilotage service. In the past there had been no ruling and pilots fought for custom with varying charges. Captain Hutchinson was a prime mover in the new arrangement.

Pilot boats needed shelter while waiting their turn to go on duty under the new scheme. The Liverpool committee of shipowners and merchants came to Anglesey in the 1770s, led by Captain Hutchinson, to examine several sites. Beaumaris, Puffin Island, Moelfre and Amlwch were among them. But the bay below Point Lynas, now called Pilots' Cove, was their final choice as it appeared to be a natural harbour which needed little attention to make it suitable.

A house was built on the promontory, with a flagstaff and colours to hoist by day, and two lanterns to be lit at night. Opposite the house, on the east side of Pilots' Cove, a slip was made from high to low watermark with a grab to heave up and launch a six oared pilot boat to board passing ships, according to Captain Hutchinson's report.

Practice proved this to be insufficient. A light was needed to shine towards the north east into Liverpool Bay so a new building was erected, on the present site of the lighthouse, rebuilt and improved in 1835. From August 1835 a strong, steady light shone out sixteen miles to sea on a fine night.

This was changed later to a flashing light.

It was thanks to Captain William Hutchinson that Anglesey's north eastern promontory was chosen for this important pilotage service over two hundred years ago.

48. Why are the Bulkeley Diaries so important to today's historians?

The diaries of William Bulkeley of Brynddu, Llanfechell, cast light on life, traditions and thought prevalent between 1735 and 1760. They give a rich account of the house, still occupied today by a descendant of the diarist, of family affairs and scandals, local political activity and farming practices. Weather patterns are noted, so is the development of the garden surrounding Brynddu by Bulkeley himself, who bought much of his stock during his visits to Ireland.

Two volumes of the diaries are in the safe-keeping of the University of Wales Bangor Library. They are a fascinating reflection on life in 18th century Anglesey, written by a strong-minded squire who was not afraid to write as he obviously spoke – plainly.

In them the reader is taken to church to suffer long, boring sermons, to Beaumaris where William attended the Sessions and the socialising which accompanied them.

We sympathise with him as he worried about the fate of his only daughter who made a disastrous marriage with the adventurer, Fortunatus Wright. We read about William's visits to Dublin relatives, where he bought plants for his garden.

His wife died when young, leaving William to see to the education of his daughter and, eventually, the care of his grand-daughter after her mother died.

The diaries tell a very human family story. The background to that story, told in the words of someone who lived through those times, make them some of Anglesey's most important documents for the historian.

49. What does the large stone arch in Holyhead harbour commemorate?

In 1821 King George IV planned a visit to Ireland. His convoy of ships was to sail to Holyhead, where he would disembark to visit Anglesey before continuing his journey to Dublin. His tour of the island was broken at Plas Newydd, the home of the 1st Marquess of Anglesey, where there would be an opportunity for representatives of all aspects of Anglesey life to pay their respects. Bonfires were lit. There was an air of expectancy. This was the first visit of a reigning monarch to the island during peace time.

The weather delayed the King's departure, and while waiting for the gale to abate His Majesty learned of the death of his Queen Caroline. Feelings between the royal couple had run high for some time, and her death appeared not to trouble him unduly. After his departure for Dublin a committee was formed to raise funds to build a triumphant arch to commemorate the visit. But times were hard and it was left to the more wealthy to contribute. Eventually sufficient money was raised and Thomas Harrison, the Chester architect who was responsible for the column to the Marquess of Anglesey at Llanfair Pwllgwyngyll, was commissioned to design the arch. This was erected where the King had stepped on to Anglesey soil.

Three years later the arch was unveiled by the Marquess before a large crowd. It later marked the terminus of Thomas Telford's London to Holyhead road.

50. There are five blue slate gravestones in Llandegfan churchyard, bearing an anchor and the names of children. What is their story?

Between 1877 and 1920 a sailing ship, the *Clio*, was moored on the Menai Strait. This was classed as 'an industrial training ship' where boys were sent to be trained as seamen. They came from a wide area – London, Manchester, and Liverpool included – from the early age of twelve, and stayed until their mid teens when their training was finished.

Conditions on board were spartan. In 1882 the Inspector of Training Schools wrote . . . 'The boys are small in size and young for a training ship although nominally over twelve years of age. The situation of the ship is stormy and exposed, too much so for the class of boys dealt with. They need every possible protection from the stiff gales and strong seas they have to battle with.'

Many of the boys were orphans, some from the workhouses or disadvantaged families. Some were sent because their social behaviour was beyond the control of their parents.

The gravestones record deaths through a variety of reasons – boys falling off rigging sixty-five to seventy feet above the deck. Illness and disease – meningitis, typhoid and tuberculosis accounted for some.

But there was one more sinister case, that of young William Brook who died in 1905, the official report reading 'as a result of concussion of the brain the result of violence by other boys'. 'Bullying has caused serious anxiety during the year but with the committal of three boys to Reformatory Schools it is hoped that this class of offence has now been effectually stamped out' concluded the report.

The inquest on William Brook resulted in 'death by misadventure'. The case did nothing to improve the standing of the training ship in the public eye. No blame was attributed to the ship's officers. It is not surprising that Anglesey mothers, at their wits' end when dealing with recalcitrant offspring, would threaten them with banishment to the *Clio*.

51. Where is 'Bedd Branwen' (Branwen's Grave)? Who was she?

'Branwen, daughter of Llŷr' is one of eleven stories of the Welsh legends, the Mabinogion.

Branwen was married to Matholwch, King of Ireland. At the wedding feast the king was insulted by her half-brother, so the Irish ill-treated her by banishing her to work in the kitchen where she was physically abused. The legend tells that she befriended a starling whom she taught to speak, and sent the bird back to Wales to her brother, Bendigeidfran (Brân) who gathered together an army and sailed to Ireland to take revenge on the Irish. In the consequent fighting Ireland was laid waste, its army defeated, and all but seven of the Welsh contingent killed in the battle. They, with Branwen, returned to Wales, landed on the west shore of Anglesey where Branwen died of a broken heart. She was buried, so the legend says, on the bank of the Alaw.

The early Bronze Age burial mound on the Alaw, dubbed 'Bedd Branwen', was re-excavated in 1967. Inroads had been made years before. This time the excavation was carried out by archaeologists from the University at Bangor. They had many interesting finds from the multiple burials and came to the conclusion that this was the burial place of a group of people, probably a single large family, living around 1400 BC.

Did Branwen ever exist, or was she merely the subject of legend? If she lived, was she buried in this multiple cist?

52. Where would you go to find 'Hendai'?

In the early years of the 14th century Edward I evicted the population of Llanfaes, sending them across Anglesey to the relatively thinly populated area of the old Welsh court known as Rhosyr on the south west coast of the island. It became known later as Newborough. The eviction robbed Llanfaes of its status as a marketing centre and allowed the town of Beaumaris to take its place.

The incomers to the Newborough area set to with a will to improve their new surroundings and make a living for themselves. The coastal strip was covered with trees and scrub. They cut down the trees and cleared away the scrub – with the help of rabbits and grazing cattle. But nature stepped in during 1330. A great storm blew in from the south west, churning up the sea which flooded the land and blew in huge quantities of sand from Caernarfon Bay which inundated their newly developed pasture and property. With no trees or scrub there was no stabilizing material left to stop the sand spreading.

During the 20th century afforestation has taken place on part of the dunes fringing the Cefni estuary. Trees now surround the remains of the 14th century 'Hendai' *(the old homes)* where emigrants from Llanfaes built their huts. Some of the foundation stones can still be seen among the trees.

A toll road leads the motorist to an official car park from where a trail leads to the site.

53. Who was Frances Williams?

There must have been many women named Frances Williams living in 19th century Anglesey, but one is remembered especially for her talents and her courage.

When the Rev. James Williams became the rector of Llanfair-yng-Nghornwy on the retirement of his father, he brought his young wife to live in the rectory in this quiet north west corner of Anglesey. She was new to the area and he was eager to show her its beauty, so one day they walked down to the coast opposite The Skerries so that she might admire the rugged coastline.

Their attention was taken by a ship in distress. The sailing packet *Alert*, on her way from Howth to Parkgate on the Wirral, had ventured close to land. She was becalmed, and as the tide was running strongly the ship was driven on to the rocks, holed, and sank immediately with the loss of one hundred and forty lives.

What should have been a pleasant afternoon outing for the young couple turned out to be a harrowing experience, as they were unable to do anything to help.

This tragedy was the catalyst for the foundation of the first lifeboat service in Anglesey, prompted by the rector and encouraged and aided by his wife.

Frances had many talents, painting being one. She had painted her version of the visit of George IV to Holyhead when he landed there three years earlier. She lithographed her painting and sold copies at seven shillings each, the money going to 'The King's Landing Fund' to reward those who saved lives and property as a result of wrecks on the coast of Anglesey and Caernarfonshire. Meanwhile her husband took it upon himself to order the first lifeboat to be stationed at Cemlyn, for which he acted as coxswain for some time.

The Skerries were part of the parish of Llanfair-yng-Nghornwy. One day a message was received to say that one of the lighthousekeepers was ill and needed medical attention. Immediately, although the weather was stormy, James and Frances launched the Cemlyn lifeboat, Frances taking with her a medicine chest to attend the sick man.

Frances encouraged their son, Owen Lloyd, to join their passion for saving life at sea, and he, too, gave brave personal service between 1853 and 1855. This Frances Williams was certainly a very special lady.

54. Oriel Ynys Môn was originally intended as a showcase for which artist's work?

Charles Tunnicliffe, wildlife artist of repute, was a Cheshire man who came to live at Malltraeth after spending many holidays there, studying birds.

He had lived in Macclesfield and taught art at Manchester Grammar School but decided to give up teaching and come to Anglesey to be a full-time artist. He was 46 years old. Painting wildlife and the landscape around his home were his main interests.

Tunnicliffe's output was phenomenal. He would study birds anatomically and in flight or at rest, and kept sketchbooks and measured drawings to which he referred constantly. His work was in great demand to illustrate books. His paintings had a wide appeal. Many were bought after his death in 1979 by the local authority in Anglesey to form a substantial and important collection and this was to form the basis of the county's treasures to be shown in the new gallery which was opened by H.M. The Queen in 1991. Changes have taken place at Oriel Ynys Môn since then, and further changes are anticipated when a new gallery is added to house the Kyffin Williams collection. But the Tunnicliffe collection is still highly prized and there is always a selection of his work to be seen there.

When Charles Tunnicliffe died in February 1979 he was almost blind, and unable to see to paint any longer.

In the prologue to his book, *A Shoreland Summer*, friend and fellow wildlife enthusiast Ian Niall wrote of him as 'an artist whose work delighted and gave great pleasure, to thousands of people not only in Britain but throughout the world'.

55. *Where is Eglwys y Bedd? For what was it once used?*

Eglwys y Bedd is the small 14th century chapel standing apart from St Cybi's church in Holyhead, near the entrance to the churchyard. It was so called as it was reputed to have been built over an ancient grave.

The building has been used in several ways over the centuries, most notably as a schoolroom in the days when the Rev. Thomas Ellis was rector at Holyhead.

Thomas Ellis came to the town in 1737 from Jesus College, Oxford. He was a character who left his mark on the town in many ways. Outspoken, he left nobody in any doubt of his criticism of the lack of morals in the town's society. He preached repentance from the pulpit, decrying the misuse of patronal festivals which had been turned into orgies.

Thomas Ellis made enemies among those who did not want the old order to change, but he made friends, too, among those who appreciated his fearlessness and longed for a cleaner society.

One of Thomas Ellis's chief interests was education. He opened a free school for the poor children of the town, held at Eglwys y Bedd, begging money for its upkeep from those he believed could afford to give. He moved to England in 1759 but his school remained until 1817 when the National School was opened. Today one of the town's schools bears his name.

56. Two shipwrecks occurred at the same place in Liverpool Bay exactly one hundred years apart ... Where and which ships?

It was October 1859 when the *Royal Charter* was on the last stage of her homeward voyage from Australia to Liverpool bringing home prospectors from the gold fields and a treasure cargo of bullion worth over £300,000. A sudden hurricane struck Liverpool Bay. Mountainous seas and storm force winds swept the ship on to the rocks at Porth Helaeth north of Moelfre. Nothing could be done to save passengers, crew, nor the ship. They were thrown into the water as the ship broke up, many to be pounded to death on the rocks or drowned.

Exactly one hundred years later the *Hindlea*, a coaster was wrecked on her way from Weston Point, Runcorn, to Newport in Gwent. Again, massive waves hit the ship during a gale, some of the waves eight metres high. This time Moelfre lifeboat made what is now regarded as a legendary effort to save the crew, with several attempts to snatch them from the wrecked vessel. At one time the lifeboat was blown on to the deck of the *Hindlea*. Eight of the crew were rescued, and shortly after the ship was hurled against the rocks before breaking in two.

This rescue had needed desperate measures. Coxswain Dick Evans lashed himself to the wheel of his lifeboat and it was his expert seamanship in terrible conditions which brought both crews to safety. The lifeboat was damaged, but the crew put to sea again immediately in answer to another call from a ship in distress.

Moelfre remembers the two events with a memorial on the cliffs above where *Royal Charter* sank, and the long and brilliant record of bravery of Coxswain Dick Evans is recalled with the striking bronze statue looking out to sea over Liverpool Bay where so many of this courageous lifeboatman's exploits took place, including the incredible rescue of the *Hindlea* crew.

57. In which Anglesey industry was a kibble used? What was it?

After Thomas Pennant visited Amlwch he described the method used to move copper ore from Parys Mountain . . . 'The ore is not got out in the common manner of mining' he wrote, 'but is cut out of the bed in the same manner as stone is out of a quarry.'

The great chasm formed by this method of mining over the years can still be seen there today.

William Bingley was another writer who visited the mine . . . 'The prospect was dreadful,' he wrote.

The ore removed by the miners was piled into large metal buckets called kibbles, and hoisted up the perpendicular side of the chasm by whimseys fixed to the upper edge. When kibbles reached the platform they were emptied into carts and the ore taken away to be processed. The kibble would then be lowered for the next load. They often had a human load, too, as this was the quickest way to descend to the floor of the opencast working. Another use for a kibble was to take workers to the staging some way down the precipice where they would be working at a level on the cliff face, perhaps cutting a cavern into the rock.

58. Which Anglesey village was associated with witchcraft?

Once, a long, long time ago says tradition, it was the custom to put those suspected of witchcraft into a rudderless and oarless boat and let the tide wash them to another shore, out of sight, out of mind.

Again according to legend, a boat came ashore on the south beach of Red Wharf Bay crammed with men and women who were weary, hungry and thirsty. Obviously they had come a distance. The people of Llanddona could not understand their language and met them with hostility. When the strangers landed they caused water to spring from the shore, so they were allowed to stay and build themselves rough shelter. The men made a living by smuggling. The women begged. If they were refused food they called a curse on the house and were accused of witchcraft. They were feared by the people of Llanddona.

One of the women, Bella, was ingenious. She changed herself into a hare and caused havoc on a farm. The angry farmer reached for his gun and, using a silver coin in place of shot, fired at her. After that, witches never troubled the people of Llanddona again.

59. What is harvested from the Menai Strait?

Yes, fish, of course, but another natural commodity which is not extracted anywhere else around the Anglesey coast – salt.

'Halen Môn' is much prized in the gourmet food world since the business was developed by the then owners of the Anglesey Sea Zoo.

David and Alison Lea Wilson met as students at the university in Bangor. Their first expedition into business came when they joined forces with a friend in an oyster farm. In 1984 they established their own Sea Zoo at Brynsiencyn, the country's first.

They visited France to see how salt was processed on the Ile de Ré. Manchester Business School ran a feasibility study, the result was encouraging. The couple took their time over the venture, analysing sea water salinity at various states of the tide, working closely with the university in Bangor and the Environment Agency. Two more years of research took place before Anglesey Sea Salt Company was formed and they felt ready to proceed.

Sea water is drawn from the Menai Strait into large setting tanks then boiled, which concentrates the brine and evaporation then begins. After seven days the crystals appear on the surface. They are then shovelled off, dried and packed.

Halen Môn is retailed widely in gourmet food shops and used by culinary experts at home and abroad.

60. In which room at Plas Newydd would you find the artist's self-portrait? Who was he?

The artist, Rex Whistler, was a friend of the Paget family of Plas Newydd. In 1936 he was invited by the 6th Marquess, who had been re-designing part of the house and had created a large dining room, to paint a picture for the long wall. This Whistler completed a few years before he died as a casualty of the Second World War. In part of that picture he included himself with a broom in hand, sweeping a flagged pavement.

Usually referred to as a mural, strictly speaking it is not, as it was painted on canvas and hung against the wall. The initial sketch was drawn on to the plaster while a piece of canvas thirty-eight feet long was woven in France and delivered to a theatre workshop in Lambeth where Whistler would have room to paint. This type of work was not unfamiliar to him, as he had been designing and painting stage settings. When almost finished the canvas was driven to Anglesey and fixed to the dining room wall where Whistler completed it.

The subject of the painting is mainly imagined, a maritime scene against a background of mountains. But one feels that the scene from the dining room window, looking over the water towards Snowdonia, could have been the inspiration. Against this maritime scene some of the activities of the Marquess and his family are depicted.

Two arcades take the scene around the corners on to the short walls of the room, as though one is looking into arcades. One pictures Lady Anglesey's pet dogs, the other Whistler with his broom. The feature which catches the attention of viewers is at the centre where Neptune has hung his crown on the top of a wall and his wet footsteps lead into the dining room and the assembled guests.

61. Who was Anglesey's famous Shakespearean actor?

When he was a school leaver, Hugh Griffith was persuaded to follow his father's profession and become a banker.

He was born at Marianglas in 1912, went to school locally and to the County School in Llangefni. As bankers did in those days he moved from branch to branch, in Llandudno, Llangefni, Mold and finally to Abersoch. Here his interest in drama became more intense as he trained young people who were members of Urdd Gobaith Cymru, the Welsh young people's movement. Griffith applied for a transfer to London, and his move there enabled him to attend night classes in drama, to visit theatres, and also to perform with The People's Theatre, a repertory company.

More success followed when he won a place at the Royal Academy of Dramatic Art out of three hundred applicants, on scholarship, and at the end of his training was awarded the Bancroft Gold Medal as the best Shakespearean actor of the year.

Hugh Griffith seldom 'rested'. He was in demand up to his war service, which took him to India and Burma, ending in South Wales.

After the war he joined the Shakespeare Memorial Company, playing King Lear to great acclaim.

Films and television followed – he won an Oscar in Hollywood for his part as the sheikh in 'Ben Hur'. Hugh Griffith died in 1980. Anglesey Borough Council mounted a plaque in his memory on the wall of his old school in Marianglas.

62. How was Telford's Holyhead Road maintained?

Telford's road across the island was divided into sections, gated with his specially designed 'sunburst' metal gates at which a toll keeper was on duty to collect tolls from road users. There were five toll houses along the Anglesey stretch of what we now call, unromantically, the A5. All were of similar design. Some are now private homes. Originally there were toll houses at Llanfair Pwllgwyngyll, Nant, Gwalchmai, Caergeiliog, and the end of the Stanley Embankment on the Holyhead side of the cob.

Tolls were collected by the Turnpike Trusts, who maintained the road surface with the proceeds. The Holyhead Road was the last in the country to be maintained in this way. In 1895 tolls came to an end.

The Llanfair Pwllgwyngyll toll house, situated where the Brynsiencyn road turns off the A5, still displays the various charges, listed on the wall of the house.

63. He lost an arm and his right eye. Holyhead friends erected a memorial to him. Who was he?

The tall obelisk memorial on the Alltran Rock, high above Holyhead at Morawelon, is a constant reminder of John Macgregor Skinner, an incomer to the island who became very well regarded in the town.

Skinner was born around 1760 in America, son of the King's Attorney General for New Jersey. He was a sailor who saw service during the American War of Independence, when he lost an arm and later his right eye.

After his naval service he came to Holyhead as captain of one of the packet boats sailing between Holyhead and Dublin, and made his home in the town. There is a drawing of the house he occupied in the local Maritime Museum.

John Macgregor Skinner lived in Holyhead for thirty-two years, making many friends and being generous in his philanthropy. He was outspoken, no holds barred, in his criticism of the postal service, always urging improvements to the ships and the passenger accommodation.

His end was tragic. Sailing home in the packet boat *Escape* he was swept into the sea when a huge wave struck the vessel off the coast of Holy Island, not far from home. There was no 'escape' for Skinner, unfortunately, and it was some time before his body was washed ashore.

The wording of the obelisk at Morawelon refers not only to his bravery, but to his 'disinterested kindness and unbounded charity'.

64. Where are there traces of the rule of the Welsh Princes?

In a field on the outskirts of Newborough are the scant remains of Llys Rhosyr, the one time manor of the Welsh Princes before Wales was subjugated by Edward I. Only the stone foundations of the wooden buildings remain, but with the help of descriptive plaques visitors can picture the site as it might have appeared when wooden superstructure made it habitable and it was a place of importance.

At the Prichard Jones Institute in Newborough there is an audio visual exhibition explaining the history of this part of Anglesey when it was one of the most important places in Wales.

At Aberffraw the Welsh Princes held their court but that, too, has almost disappeared. Traces remain under a modern housing estate, but a commemorative stone on the estate reminds passers-by that some foundations may still be lying beneath the houses.

After the last Prince, Llywelyn, died in 1288 and Edward introduced the English legal system into Wales, local administration on Anglesey was transferred to Beaumaris and the Aberffraw court ceased to exist.

A leaflet is available from Tourist Information Centres giving directions to Llys Rhosyr.

65. This is a specialised geological centre, open to the public. Where is it?

Stone Science Museum was opened at 'Bryn Eglwys', Talwrn, a former rectory, in 1989, by the owner, Dave Wilson. Its fame has spread. Now Dave welcomes forty thousand visitors a year to see the displays and buy in the shop from his vast collections and a range of books on the subjects of geology and local history. He has been in the business of selling fossils and minerals worldwide since 1971.

The first Victorian rector to live at 'Bryn Eglwys' when the house was built in 1870 would scarcely recognise the interior today, as each room occupied by the business and the museum is crammed with treasures to interest adults and children alike, many of which are on sale.

Dave Wilson is especially proud of his display of rare fossils of fish from Lebanon, which, he claims, is the best in the world. There is also a colourful display of American Indian artefacts, one of very few such displays outside America.

In the grounds visitors can see a reconstruction of an Iron Age rush-thatched roundhouse.

'Bryn Eglwys' is the large house standing to the left of a sweeping bend in the B5109 country road from Pentraeth to Llangefni, at Talwrn. There is ample car parking space outside the house.

66. Which lighthouse welcomes the public?

Following the automation of lighthouses around the British coast Trinity House, the owners, encourage visits to a select few where the work of the agency is explained and visitors learn of its history. South Stack, close to Holyhead, is one of these. With the collaboration of Ynys Môn County Council visitors are now able to join guided tours at specific times between Easter and the beginning of September.

South Stack, dramatically situated on its own small rocky island, has been a waymark for coastal traffic and a landmark and orientation light for vessels crossing the Irish Sea since the light first shone there in 1809.

Trinity House had leased the island earlier, and commissioned Daniel Alexander, their consultant engineer, to design this, his first lighthouse. He was to design several more. Joseph Nelson of Leeds was the builder. South Stack was the first of fifteen he built for Trinity House.

Conveying materials to the island brought seemingly insurmountable problems. Four hundred steps had to be hacked into the rock on the steep side of Holyhead Mountain and the chasm between them and the small island spanned. Those four hundred steps are still used as the approach, today, but crossing is made easier by a substantial new bridge.

The problems of building are explained on the guided tour. Visitors are allowed up to the top of the tower to see the lantern at close quarters. Today the tower flashes a white light every ten seconds. This can be seen over twenty nautical miles in clear weather.

Then visitors return across the new bridge, back to the mainland – up those four hundred steps!

This is certainly an experience not to be missed. Leaflets giving opening times are available from Tourist Information

Centres. When the light is being serviced South Stack is closed to public viewing, but prior warning is always given at the ticket office near the car park.

67. Which Anglesey church is famous for its woodcarving?

Saint Eilian's church at Llaneilian, near Amlwch, has an unrivalled collection of woodcarvings. The wooden rood screen has a painting of a skeleton. The church has some unique antiques and a dugout oak chest bearing the date 1667.

This is a 12th/15th century medieval building, believed to have been built on the site of a 'clas' church of a much earlier date. A 14th century chapel is set at an angle to the chancel, reached through a short connecting passage. The tower is capped by an unusual pyramidal spire. This is the 12th century part of the building.

Saint Eilian's church is Grade A listed today, judged to be one of the most interesting in Anglesey.

Tradition tells that the 6th century saint brought his family, all their goods and stock, by sea to land at Porth yr Ychen nearby, and there he built his oratory, gaining a reputation for sanctity and his ability to cure ailments.

The screen, the loft, the chancel stalls and the shrine pedestal in the chapel are all of wood. The roof of the chancel is cambered-beam. Wooden angels abound, some playing flutes and bagpipes, others holding shields or praying. The painted skeleton holds a scroll on which is written 'Colyn Angau yw pechod' . . . we might interpret it loosely as *'The wages of sin is death'*, a stern reminder to those approaching the altar.

68. What began with a chicken's broken leg?

The story really begins before the chicken broke its leg. One dark, stormy night when Danny Lukie, a smuggler, sailed in his boat from the north coast to meet a ship carrying contraband, he came across a vessel in distress. She was about to sink with a man and two boys on board. As the ship disappeared under the wave, the man died, but Lukie managed to rescue the two boys. He took them ashore, to the home of Dr Lloyd at Mynachdy. The boys spoke Spanish but no English. One was adopted by a local family at a farm nearby called Maes and given the name Evan Thomas. He helped around the house and grounds of Mynachdy, learnt to speak Welsh and showed great interest in the doctor's work.

One day Dr Lloyd noticed how Evan treated the broken leg of one of his chickens, and it was obvious that the boy had a gift of bone-setting, so he took him along to patients with fractured limbs which needed setting.

As Evan Thomas grew to manhood he was much in demand in Anglesey and, as his reputation spread, farther afield. He married a local girl and their children also had the same gift.

After Evan's death in 1819 Viscount Bulkeley had a memorial stone erected in Llanfair-yng-Nghornwy where Evan was buried, with this inscription . . .

'To the memory of Evan Thomas of Maes in This Parish who, in humble life, without the aid of Education or any other Advantage, by an extraordinary gift of Nature Acquired such a knowledge of the Human Frame as to become a most skilled Bonesetter whereby he rendered himself Preeminently useful to his Fellow Creatures.'

Evan Thomas was an ancestor of the Liverpool surgeon Hugh Owen Thomas who devised surgical appliances and carried on a busy orthopaedic practice in the city. His treatments obviated many operations where patients might otherwise have lost a limb.

Hugh Owen Thomas's nephew, Sir Robert Jones, another orthopaedic surgeon, will always be associated with the world-famous orthopaedic hospital at Gobowen which he had helped to set up.

69. Who were the Crigyll Robbers?

In the days of sail the Anglesey coastal seabed was littered with wrecks as frail craft succumbed to storms. It was the custom for local people, poor as they were, to beachcomb after a stormy night, to search for any useful jetsam which may have been washed ashore from a wrecked ship. This was illegal, as all property from wrecks was deemed to be government owned, but little notice was taken of the law. It was even the practice to entice ships to their doom in the hope that the wreckage would reveal items worth collecting.

To accomplish this they used 'Cornish Lamping' whereby lamps were tied to the bodies of grazing cattle so that, as the cattle moved, they would appear like ships' lanterns bobbing up and down while in harbour. Sea-charting was almost non-existent in those days and there were no beacons to guide ships at night, so the ruse often worked and ships were drawn on to submerged rocks close to the shore.

In 1740 members of a gang called the Crigyll Robbers (Lladron Crigyll) were caught, accused of plundering the ship Loveday and Betty. The men were tried at Beaumaris court but acquitted by a jury who were terrorised by the men's supporters, such was the determination of a desperately poor community to be assured that their self-attributed right to plunder would be upheld.

70. What is unique about Nant y Pandy?

Nant y Pandy is a steep-sided gorge on the outskirts of Llangefni, formed during the ice-age as meltwater raced along and carved a passage. The name, Nant y Pandy, means the brook of the fulling mill – the wool-processing mill which once worked busily at the head of the valley. For years Nant y Pandy was referred to as 'The Dingle' but Llangefni now reverts to the Welsh name.

Nant y Pandy is now a local nature reserve, walked by many who appreciate the wildlife and history. Recent community involvement, working in partnership and by grant aid with environment agencies, it has seen many improvements to retain the wildlife interest including wooden boardwalks and three new bridges.

The unique addition to these amenities has been a collection of eye-catching sculptures. At the Station gateway there is an innovative introduction using twenty-five oak trunks, each sliced lengthways to reveal certain elements of Anglesey's industrial and cultural history. This has been designed and made by Nigel Talbot.

Reece Ingram, at the Church gateway, has chosen the dragonfly as his design feature, as these can be seen in Nant y Pandy and are a constant source of delight to walkers.

At the Coed Plas entrance flowers provide the theme of Dominic Clare's sculpture. The plant forms are enlarged to larger-than-life to emphasise their beauty.

Nant y Pandy is managed by Ynys Môn County Council's Countryside Service. It is proving to be a popular place for a quiet stroll.

71. *Who were the first to walk over the Menai Strait?*

Thomas Telford, the designer of the Menai Suspension Bridge, you might say. No.

On April 15th, 1822, the day the first chain was thrown across the Strait was an occasion for celebration. Flags flew, crowds of onlookers gathered, there was excitement in the air. The end of the chain to be drawn across was put on to a raft and towed to mid-stream by four boats then tied to several buoys. Another chain hung from the pier on the Bangor side almost down to high water. The end of the chain on the raft was fastened to two blocks so that it could be hoisted to the top of the pier on the Anglesey side. It was a complicated operation, worked out to the split second by Telford and his engineers. Then began the hoisting procedure as twenty-eight men worked four capstans, Telford himself was on hand to join the two chains together and there was loud cheering as the chains rose into position.

Then came the unexpected drama. The crowd, silent in fear, watched as three of the workers – a labourer, a stonemason and a carpenter – crept slowly along the chain to the opposite side while a band played below them.

Unpredictable and foolish, perhaps, but an unforgettable sight to the watching crowd and, no doubt, to Telford himself.

72. *Where can you see a few items saved from the wreck of* Royal Charter?

Most of the artefacts found by the wreck in later years are at the Maritime Museum in Liverpool, but a few are on display at Moelfre Seawatch Centre, poignant in their rarity. Some gold coins, pieces of jewellery and buttons tell a sad, silent tale.

Those who have seen the very credible make-up of a corner of the deck of a sailing ship on show at Oriel Ynys Môn, and remember the sound of creaking timbers in a gale force wind which accompanies it, will be able to imagine to some extent that voyage with so many returning to Britain from Australia, only to be pitched into the sea a matter of a few miles from their destination on that dark, stormy night in 1859. Their story has become a legend.

The Moelfre Seawatch Centre has much to interest the maritime historian – artefacts from wrecks, photographs, stories of the exploits of the famous Moelfre lifeboats and their courageous crews over the years. An Oakeley-class self-righting unsinkable lifeboat of the last century takes pride of place on its stocks in the centre of the room, ready to display its more modern equipment to curious viewers. In the horrendous situation of that dreadful night of 1859 one can well believe that even the more sophisticated lifeboat as this could have been of little help to the ill-fated passengers of *Royal Charter*.

73. Where is Anglesey's only known motte and bailey castle?

The river Lleiniog makes its way to the sea after leaving Llangoed, down a valley with a steep slope on one side and the road to the coast on the other.

In years past the Lleiniog valley was a creek, filled with water at high tide, so Castell Aberlleiniog, high on top of the sloped side, was strategically placed to meet any invasion. Originally Norman, now only a shadow of its former self, it has had additions over the centuries. It was built in the 11th century by the Norman Earl of Chester, that unpopular Hugh Lupus, but attacked and conquered by Gruffydd ap Cynan, Lord of Gwynedd, who burnt it in 1094.

A low stone keep was built later, and this was used as a fort, occupied during the Civil Wars.

Today restoration is taking place with a view to making Aberlleiniog accessible to the public as one of Anglesey's heritage sites. The sea no longer encroaches. The river Lleiniog runs unhampered along the valley, leaving nature – plants, birds and wildlife – a free rein.

74. There is a polished granite memorial in a Holy Island churchyard in memory of five men. Where is it? Who were they?

The memorial stands outside Saint Gwenfaen's church at Rhoscolyn, perpetuating the memory of five brave lifeboatmen who were drowned during service.

The tragedy happened in 1920 when the *Ramon Cabrera* lifeboat was called out in atrocious weather to rescue the crew of the steamer *Timbo*. But strong winds and huge seas made the task hopeless and the lifeboat had to put in to Llanddwyn to shelter.

Two of the lifeboatmen were washed overboard and drowned. Two miles from the shore a massive wave threw the lifeboat on to her beam and as she righted herself three more of the crew were swept in to the water and they, too, drowned.

The bodies of the men were later recovered and buried at Rhoscolyn. The Rhoscolyn lifeboat station closed in 1929. Since it opened in 1830 fifty-eight lives were saved.

75. Where is there a Grade II listed building resembling an upturned boat hull?

The Catholic community in Amlwch worship at their church dedicated to Our Lady Star of the Sea and Saint Winifrede, on the outskirts of the town towards Bull Bay.

The architect, Guiseppe Rinvolucri, created an unusual design representing an upturned boat hull with round porthole windows to underline its nearness to the sea. The building created a stir when it was consecrated in 1937, because of its daring design, and as it was constructed from reinforced concrete.

In recent years fabric problems and difficult access for the disabled have put the future of the building in jeopardy – the cost of restoration and bringing the church's facilities up-to-date within recent legislation would be enormous.

The architect was born in Italy in 1891, but lived in Conwy. He died in 1963.

76. Who was the famous Welsh composer who lived at Menai Bridge?

The music of William Mathias is known worldwide.

He was born in Whitland, Dyfed, in 1934, and educated at University College of Wales, Aberystwyth and the Royal Academy of Music in London. His first lectureship was at University College of North Wales Bangor, 1959-68, then he held the post of senior lecturer in composition at Edinburgh between 1968 and 1970. He returned to Bangor in 1970 to occupy the chair of music and came to live in Menai Bridge.

His many compositions include orchestral works, concertos, chamber music, choral and church music and pieces for the organ.

After retirement William Mathias remained in Menai Bridge until his death in 1992. During his latter years he was artistic director for the North Wales Music Festival held at St Asaph Cathedral.

77. Where was an old hulk used to help dam the tide?

Before 1788 a high tide carried seawater almost twelve miles inland from the Cefni estuary towards Llangefni. What is now green grassland was the Cors Ddaugau marsh, difficult to cross in most weather, especially for cattle on their way to the market at Caernarfon.

But 1788 saw the Malltraeth and Cors Ddaugau Act passed and a great plan of drainage for the area. It was intended to build an embankment to stop the tide encroaching on the land, using a base of furze faggots bound with cordage and covered with sand and turf sods, topped with a stone pavement. This was no simple task. Work began on both sides of the river at once, meeting in the middle where the force of water would be greatest. It was almost complete in January 1796 when an unusually high tide broke through and work was halted.

Even in those far off days, costs rose year by year, and the money was not available for work to continue. The breach remained until 1811 when another Act allowed permission to raise more money from local landowners, so work then began again. The difficulty of filling the final breach was overcome by jamming an old hulk brought from Caernarfon and filling it with rubble. A year later the embankment was complete and a road constructed between Malltraeth and Newborough. River Cefni was channelled on a straight line with embankments on each side to prevent any excess water flooding the land, thus giving landowners of the marsh the advantage of more grazing.

78. Where could you once enjoy a whitebait tea?

Ynys Gorad Goch, the largest of several islands in the Menai Strait, between the two bridges, was the site of an ancient fish weir. There were others along this stretch of water, at Porthaethwy and Bangor.

The island has a long history. The earliest known document relating to the fishery dated 1590 tells that it belonged to the Bangor diocese. The white painted buildings include a room with a central window over which there is a carving of a mitre and the inscription I.R. 1808, referring to the then Bishop of Bangor who used the room for meditation.

Weir fishing is an ancient craft. Here the tides were used to catch fish as they passed through the water. Fish caught in the weirs in earlier times were taken to the various religious settlements hereabouts. Later they were sold at the markets. Curing took place in the tower on the island.

After diocesan ownership ceased Ynys Gorad Goch passed into private hands and the family living there did a popular summer trade by serving whitebait teas to visitors. On a pleasant Sunday afternoon it was a great attraction.

Visitors would walk down to the shore through the Coed Môr woods, ring a bell hanging from a tree to summon a boat to take them across to enjoy a pot of tea, brown bread and butter and fried fresh whitebait in a basket, all for one shilling.

During the middle of the last century successful efforts were made to develop a garden around the buildings, not easy because of strong winds and sometimes rough weather in such an exposed position.

79. Who was the self-styled 'Bishop of Anglesey'?

When Nonconformity swept into Anglesey in the late 18th, the 19th and early 20th centuries preachers conveyed their message with high drama – an attitude appreciated by worshippers who had hitherto been bored by the lengthy and uninteresting sermons of the clergy of the established church.

One of these charismatic preachers was the Rev. Christmas Evans, a Baptist from south Wales, a one-time farm labourer who was ordained in 1798.

Baptist chapels were built at Cildwrn, Llangefni, and Mynydd Parys, Amlwch. They were well supported by the new nonconformists of that persuasion who invited the newly-ordained preacher whose fame had penetrated to north Wales to minister in Anglesey.

Christmas Evans' oratory was fiery; he pulled no punches in the pulpit. But as his popularity grew so did his ego. Before long he was referring to himself as a newly proclaimed 'Bishop of Anglesey'. Along with his growing self-confidence came a dictatorial attitude which was against the principles of some of his congregations at Llangefni and Amlwch, and his popularity began to wane. He left the island to undertake ministries in south Wales, and died in Swansea in 1838 while on a preaching tour.

80. Which treasured maritime documents came to Anglesey as a result of a recent auction at Sotheby's?

A joint bid by Ynys Môn County Council and Cymdeithas y Morrisiaid *(the Morris Society)* has brought back to Anglesey Lewis Morris's book *Plans of Harbours* and a chart of the west coast of Wales created by him in the 18th century.

Plans and coastal charts were then virtually unknown to those sailing the Welsh coastline so Lewis Morris's work did much to ensure greater safety for vessels and their crews.

The items had been part of a large private collection of maps and books, and can now be seen at the Ynys Môn Record Office in Llangefni.

81. Which Royal Yacht sank near The Skerries and when?

It was in March 1675 when the *Mary* sank between The Skerries and the mainland shore. She had been put into service on the Irish route but her story began some time before when she was presented to King Charles on his accession to the English throne by William of Holland as a gift.

She was a large vessel, manned by a crew of thirty, but found to be unsuitable for use in the river Thames so was diverted to the Irish crossing to serve the more important passengers between England and Dublin.

As she keeled over, her tall mast struck The Skerries rocks and those who were able scrambled along it to reach safety. Not all were so fortunate, however, and many drowned. But the story of the *Mary* does not end there.

In 1991 two of her guns were found on the seabed by sub-aqua divers, and the search began for other treasures.

When brought to the surface they were taken to the Maritime Museum in Liverpool. Among the hoard were more guns, an anchor, some silver coins, tableware and jewellery. There was one other find to underline the human tragedy – the skeleton of a woman passenger. A rigging shot from the *Mary* is displayed at the Moelfre Seawatch Centre.

82. School slates and slate pencils were made here. Where?

Pwllfanog is a tiny creek on the Anglesey shore of the Menai Strait not far from Llanfair Pwllgwyngyll and the Britannia Bridge. A group of cottages and the remains of industrial buildings are gathered together close to the Plas Newydd estate boundary wall.

This was once a busy little port with sailing ships delivering slate from the Caernarfonshire quarries to the factory on the quayside, and loading dressed school slates in their wooden frames, and slate pencils, bound for markets elsewhere.

During the 19th century a water-powered flour mill was in full production, there was a bacon factory, coal was delivered to be carted away to the villages nearby to keep home fires burning. Later a margarine factory was opened and a building where chicory could be dried and roasted. A cookshop and a tavern, 'The Pilot Boat', were two amenities added for the benefit of workers and residents of the cottages.

83. What is the story of Ellin's tower?

Ellin's tower, the building sitting comfortably on the top of the cliffs looking out on to South Stack and the Irish Sea, was built as a summer retreat for Ellin, the wife of William Owen Stanley of Penrhos. Here Ellin would relax, away from the cares of a chatelaine of a great house, and the many charitable works she undertook in Holyhead in that capacity.

Ellin was the daughter of Sir John Williams of Bodelwyddan. She met her future husband when she was Patroness of the Anglesey Hunt Club in 1832, and he was Deputy Comptroller. The Club was regarded as an unofficial marriage bureau among the upper middle class of north Wales.

She and William Owen Stanley were highly regarded in Holyhead.

Ellin's tower is now an RSPB centre where thousands visit every year in the spring and summer, to watch birds nesting on cliff crevices, seen through the Society's binoculars.

84. She's a working ship with a royal name. Where might you see her?

The neat ship *Prince Madog* can sometimes be seen at the Princess Pier at Menai Bridge, when not involved in practical exercises at sea. The present *Prince Madog* replaced an earlier vessel of the same name at the turn of this century.

The name probably refers to the Prince Madog, Madog ap Owain Gwynedd, who was one of the early adventurers searching for the north-west passage. It was once claimed that he was the founder of the first Welsh community to settle in America, during the 12th century.

This new ship is a highly sophisticated vessel, costing £3.5m, ocean-going, a floating laboratory, used by students and researchers of the Ocean Sciences department of University of Wales Bangor.

The Ocean Sciences department at Bangor is one of the largest University departments teaching marine sciences in Britain, and among the largest in Europe. The department building stands a few metres from the Menai Strait at Menai Bridge.

85. This was described by a newspaper of 1846 as being used by 'connoisseurs throughout the three Kingdoms'. To which product did this refer?

During the middle of the 19th century snuff taking was popular, as was smoking tobacco. There was a lucrative snuff processing industry at Llannerch-y-medd – 'high dried toast Welsh Lundyfoot, alias Llwch Mân Llannerchymedd'.

At nearby Amlwch tobacco processing took place, a product patronised widely, no doubt, by the vast influx of workers to the Mynydd Parys copper mines.

In his Royal Commission on Labour Report to the Government of 1853, D. Lleufer Thomas wrote . . .

'Practically everyone smokes or chews or does both. By the end of each meeting I held the floor of the room was covered with tobacco spittle. Some of the sleeping places that I also inspected were well stained with the same juice. Apart from the constant drain which this excessive use of tobacco entails, it must be injurious to the health of the younger lads as well as being filthy in the extreme.'

Snuff manufacture in Llannerch-y-medd was short lived. Attempts were made in 1865 to revive it, but by that time the fashion had ended.

86. Where will you see an early burial site, the remains of a medieval chapel and a substantial hut group close together?

Lligwy, lying close to Llanallgo, is famed for its ancient monuments. The great burial site of the Neolithic period has a huge capstone covering a rock-cut chamber, the stone weighing several tons, posing the question – how was it lifted into place, and who was buried there?

There were two groups of burials here, numbering up to thirty people. The chamber was excavated in 1909 when the remains of men, women and children were found, also an assortment of flints and pottery. The capstone perches on three smaller yet still large stones.

Capel Lligwy, near the pathway to Din Lligwy, is of 12th century origin, but was enlarged over the centuries. Now roofless, it is nevertheless a striking small chapel in a green field edged with trees.

The pathway leads to Din Lligwy, a Romano-British hut group which, say archaeologists, may well have been an earlier site long since abandoned, as early implements have been found there. The foundations of the huts can be seen clearly. The visitor is left in no doubt that it was once a thriving farming community.

87. Why is Anglesey favoured by walkers?

Collaboration between several agencies has resulted in 'The Isle of Anglesey Coastal Path' reaching reality.

Anglesey's coast is around 125 miles long. The coastal path affords walkers a superb way of seeing and appreciating the island, as it is a combination of permissive paths and public rights of way, displaying many wonderful features – seascapes, landscapes, designated areas of outstanding national beauty, yet never far from villages and public transport so that walks can be done in sections.

The whole project has been supported partly by a European funded scheme, by agencies such as the National Trust and Forest Enterprise and the Environment Agency, with Menter Môn undertaking the planning which has been done successfully through close association with farmers and environmentalists.

The official starting point is Saint Cybi's church in Holyhead. There are twenty villages and towns along the way. Walkers can buy useful map-guides to sections of the path (twelve in all) from Tourist Information Centres on the island. These show where there is parking, where toilets, pubs and refreshments can be found, any sites and buildings of special interest, and nearest bus stops to the pathway with the numbers of service buses stopping there.

The guides are printed sectionally so that the whole distance may be covered with planning, to be completed at leisure over several days or weeks. There is also a coastal path guidebook available from Tourist Information Centres price £9.99 which gives the background to what the walker will see on the way.

88. This garden near Cemaes is open to the public once a year. What is its name?

Cestyll was a house standing in open country between Cemaes and Cemlyn, bought by the Hon. William Walter Vivian of Glyn, Bangor, who gave it to his favourite niece, Violet, daughter of Lord Vivian of Bodmin.

Today, the property belongs to the nuclear power station authority at Wylfa. The garden is open to the public, once a year, so perpetuating Violet Vivian's custom during her lifetime.

The garden is virtually a rock garden, which lies down a narrow valley to the sea, with the little Afon Cafnan running through it. Visitors flock here on Open Day in the spring, when the garden is at its best, to enjoy what in effect is Violet Vivian's creation. She used Cestyll as a summer home, beginning in earnest to develop her garden in 1922. Some 3,000 bedding plants were planted out each spring. She also planted a group of fir trees to provide a windbreak and had soil carried to the rocks for a rock garden.

Although she never lived there for any length of time, Cestyll was a favourite place to come to relax, away from her busy, demanding social life in London where she was Maid of Honour to Queen Alexandra for over twenty years. She was particularly friendly with Princess Victoria who also spent many happy hours in the Cestyll garden.

After her death Cestyll was inherited by Lady Astor, and from there it became part of the Wylfa estate under the ownership of the nuclear power station, who continue to care for the garden with the help of staff and volunteers. Today, visitors can enjoy it once a year, as Violet Vivian would have wished.

The mill on the shore is not part of Cestyll garden but is now owned by the National Trust and never opened to the public.

89. This is a building on a beach, looking out across a bay. Where is it? What is it?

There are maritime museums in many of our seaside towns, all telling lively stories of years of sea-faring but there is none, surely, as all-encompassing yet reflecting the story of a port in a relatively small space, than that at Holyhead.

For some years Holyhead Maritime Museum was situated in Kingsland, some way from the harbour, but as soon as the present building, the old lifeboat house, became available, and the move was made, people became aware of it and its future was assured. This is where you can grasp the importance of the sea-faring history of Holyhead in a short time, from its early days through two world wars, up to the present day.

Recent refurbishing and extension have made it a delightful place to spend an hour or two – with the possibility of refreshment to follow in the newly leased café which perches, literally, above the water, the view from its picture window extending across the New Harbour to the Breakwater lighthouse.

There is no doubt about it, Holyhead Maritime Museum is a worthwhile addition to Newry Beach.

90. Who were the two sisters who became famous for their botanical illustrations?

The Massey sisters, Edith and Gwenddolen, lived at 'Cornelyn', a large house at Llangoed where the family had come to live from Cheshire. This was in 1890. Both sisters enjoyed a comfortable life with parents to whom money appears to have been little object. Both were keen artists, specialising in the plants and flowers of Anglesey. Oriel

Ynys Môn in Llangefni has a large collection of their work, prints of which are proving as popular today as they ever were. They spent hours at a small cottage on the shore of the Menai Strait, painting. The Llangefni collection now numbers over five hundred.

Edith and Gwenddolen remained spinsters, enjoying riding and mixing with their own social class. Both died during the 1940s.

91. Where are Anglesey's 'mountains'?

Being a relatively flat county, one might not expect to find mountains in Anglesey, but all is relative. Local Anglesey people have always referred to the higher land on their island as 'mountains'.

There is Mynydd Twr (*Holyhead Mountain*), for instance, that great hump of rocky land overlooking the port immediately below. Mynydd y Garn, on the other side of Holyhead Bay to the north, looking down on the tiny village of Llanfair-yng-Nghornwy on one side and over to the Skerries to the north. Mynydd Mechell is the hilly agricultural area around Llanfechell, a tract of land between two small lakes. Mynydd Parys – everyone knows – was the area where copper mining took place during the 19th century. Mynydd Eilian rises above Llaneilian, looking across to Point Lynas. Mynydd Bodafon, approached from Brynteg or Maenaddwyn, offers a superb view of the whole of Anglesey from its summit which is a brief and easy climb from the quiet B-road around its foot. Mynydd Llwydiarth on the eastern side of Anglesey overlooks Traeth Coch (*Red Wharf Bay*). It can appear sombre and almost forbidding on a dull day, crowned as it is with trees which hide early settlement. Our forefathers liked their hilltops. They found them in Anglesey.

92. *Where will you find a stately home for pigeons?*

The dovecote at Penmon, not within the walls of the Priory but on the other side of the lane leading to Penmon Point, is always an attraction to visitors who peer through its open doorway at the vaulted interior, marvelling at the workmanship which went in to creating a stone resting place for one thousand birds in holes and on ledges around the walls. A stone pillar rises up the centre of the building. This once supported a ladder which could be moved around to remove eggs from the nests. They were a much appreciated addition to the diet in 1500 when the dovecote was built by the local squire. No doubt he also enjoyed pigeon pie.

93. *Who was the Copper King?*

His was the story of 'local boy made good'. Thomas Williams was born in the farming community of Llansadwrn, where he went to school. This was in 1838. He became a lawyer, but in later life he was more than that. Today we should call him a capitalist.

Thomas Williams saw the profitability of establishing the copper industry at Parys Mountain, at a time when the country's navy was deciding to copper-bottom its ships and the development of the mine on Parys Mountain brought work to hundreds, as well as making Thomas a rich man.

His initiative made him look to other interests over a wide area of Britain. He died a millionaire.

Thomas Williams had a reputation for fair dealing, both with his customers and his workforce, and he was dubbed in Welsh 'Twm Chwarae Teg' (*Tom Fair Play*).

Towards the end of his life he acquired an estate at

Llanidan, where he died and was buried in the churchyard there. But some years later his body was exhumed, and re-buried at Llandegfan with his son.

94. *Where are there two ten-foot high standing stones?*

There are many hut circles and ancient monuments on Anglesey, but the site at Penrhosfeilw on Holy Island is unique as it is now in an RSPB nature reserve where public access has been allowed since 2005.

The site is famous for its henge monuments, two tall standing stones. The word 'henge' comes from the name Stonehenge. Archaeologists think they may have been open air sanctuaries where rituals took place. Their use is still a cause for conjecture.

Holy Island is rich in early monuments and hut circles. One of those nearby Penrhosfeilw is the so-called Irishmen's Huts *(Cytiau'r Gwyddelod)*. The Tŷ Mawr hut site dates back some 2500 years. It is a collection of around eight huts separated by terraced fields. Although excavations took place during the 1860s nothing bearing any resemblance to Irish artefacts have been found here. But the Welsh name certainly reminds us of the proximity of Ireland from where there must have been traffic of people and goods even in those early days.

At Trearddur Bay the Tywyn y Capel site has been excavated more recently. There was a Celtic chapel and burial ground there. The mound is said to have been the spot where Saint Bridget, patron saint of Ireland, first set foot on Welsh ground. Today there is a modern Celtic cross to mark the place, with inscriptions in Welsh, Latin and English.

95. *These two lighthouses stand not far from each other.*

At Llanddwyn, where land stretches out into the Irish Sea in a long finger, the entrance to the Menai Strait has always been a dangerous area for shipping to negotiate tides and weather combining to make it so. In the days of sail there were many and frequent shipwrecks.

Tŵr Bach *(the Little Tower)* was the first to be built, more of a beacon than a lighthouse, to guide ships into Caernarfon Bay and harbour, but it was soon found to be ineffectual and a better light, which carried further, was planned.

In 1845 Tŵr Mawr *(the Large Tower)* was built on higher land, its light to shine out over the Irish Sea. In 1845, sailing ships were predominant and were in need of special guidance.

At one time Llanddwyn Island was busy, with a lifeboat station and a pilotage service, the pilots living in the cottages now occupied during the summer by the nature reserve warden and housing a small exhibition. When the lifeboat operated the crew were assembled from their homes in Newborough, some distance away. They were called by firing a cannon which can still be seen on the island.

96. There were once many of these on Anglesey. Now only this one works. What? Where?

Visitors to Anglesey today remark on the many windmill relics, sad-looking towers with their caps and sails long disappeared.

At one time the island was a corn-producing county. The island was, and still is, at the mercy of the wind. Many years ago Anglesey produced more grain than any other part of Wales. Water power was preferred in mills elsewhere, as there was plenty to drive the wheels which turned the machinery to grind the corn, but here in Anglesey millers had to depend on the wind as water was usually in short supply. Melin Llynnon at Llanddeusant was one of these, and the last to work. Built during 1885-6 this great stone tower was damaged in a storm in 1918, when its huge sails were damaged beyond repair. For many years all that remained was the shell of the building, the cast iron windshaft and the cross.

In 1978 Anglesey Borough Council decided to restore Llynnon Mill, and today it is one of the island's most popular tourist attractions. When wind force allows the sails turn again and flour is produced, which can be bought in the shop. The excitement of seeing the great sails turning in the wind is an experience!

97. He's sculpted in bronze, looking out to sea. Who was he?

The name Dick Evans is known to every lifeboatman on and around the coast of Anglesey and even farther afield. He was coxswain of the Moelfre lifeboat for many years, undertaking some hair-raising rescues at sea in the dangerous waters of Liverpool Bay. The huge bronze statue stands on the cliff not far from the lifeboat house and is a reminder, if any were indeed needed, of this man's superb courage and seamanship.

This is the coast where 'Royal Charter' was last seen during the 19th century, when she perished in a hurricane. Exactly one hundred years later, in 1959, the 'Hindlea' was caught in a hurricane at the same spot.

Dick Evans took the Moelfre lifeboat to the aid of the sinking ship. The sea was mountainous. At one time the lifeboat was swept up on to the deck of the fated 'Hindlea', but through all their problems the lifeboat managed to save all eight members of the crew before she broke her back and disappeared below the waves. Dick Evans took his lifeboat back to land his thankful passengers at Moelfre, his boat damaged, but left again immediately to answer another call.

He received every honour from the RNLI for his years of service.

The statue was unveiled after Dick Evans's death by HRH The Prince of Wales, who spoke warmly of this brave man's courage and service.

98. Where would you pick oakum?

No, not along the roadside, nor in the forest. And not along the banks of one of Anglesey's many lakes. If you picked oakum you were a criminal, and would be made to do so in Beaumaris gaol as part of your sentence. It was one of the unpleasant chores which prisoners had to undertake along with stone-shattering and spending time on the treadwheel.

Oakum picking was tedious work which wore the finger ends until they were sore. Oakum was ship's cable, a tough rope which came in bundles of small pieces to the gaol. These had to be unravelled. The resulting strands were used for caulking vessels. Some of the pieces were knotted twine, very difficult to unravel. Some were tarred, too, which made the job even more unpleasant. And all this had to be done in silence. The hours were long. There was little or no respite.

Today visitors to the gaol, open to the public, can read a description of the work in the prison workroom. It takes only a little imagination to picture the scene.

99. She gave Liberal service to Anglesey. Who was she?

In 1929 Megan Lloyd George was elected Member of Parliament for Anglesey, the first woman Member of Parliament to be elected in Wales. She was a regular contributor to debates in the House of Commons when they concerned Welsh affairs, agriculture and unemployment.

She became Lady Megan in 1945 when her father was created an Earl.

By this time her political tendencies turned towards the left and at one time it was thought that she might change her loyalties and join the Labour Party, but Clement Davies saved the day for the Liberal Party when he appointed her leader of the Parliamentary Liberal Party. This appointment, however, was short-lived as Lady Megan lost her Anglesey seat in the next election to Cledwyn Hughes (Labour). In 1957 she did join the Labour ranks and was elected Member of Parliament for Carmarthen, a seat she held until she died in 1966.

100. Which one-time convent chapel has been converted into a successful community centre?

The Ucheldre Centre in Holyhead – well named because it stands at the high-point of the town – came into being after the Convent School closed in 1988. The school had been run by a French Roman Catholic order of nuns, the Sisters of Bon Sauveur. There was a beautiful chapel on the site too. During this time Holyhead was a severely depressed town and some residents were fearful for its future. So they banded together with the intention of saving what was left of the buildings after the school was demolished and creating a new concept – a centre for arts and events, exhibitions and other activities of an educational and multi-purpose character. It would be unique in Anglesey.

Sheltered housing was built on part of the extensive site in Millbank. The enthusiasts' project meant that the chapel would be saved from a fate like that of the school as it could be adapted for use as a hall and meeting place without losing any of its architectural beauty.

The project was planned in 1989. By 2008 it is well established and known and admired beyond Anglesey. Its pleasant garden with a small amphitheatre for outdoor events, a well stocked shop, and a restaurant which has long since made a name for itself for quality meals, now add to the success of the Ucheldre Centre, which is open and run by volunteers and a small regular staff throughout the year. Maintenance of the Centre is funded by several public bodies and from money raised by its own events.

Acknowledgements

Thanks are due to many people, particularly those who have researched in the past and written of their experiences and the knowledge they gained. Also The Countryside Council for Wales; Alun Gruffydd, one-time curator at Oriel Ynys Môn and his staff; the staffs of Menai Bridge, Llangefni and Holyhead libraries for their untiring attention; to John C. Davies of Holyhead and Ed Pari Jones, Llanfair Pwllgwyngyll, for permission to use photographs. Working with Gwasg Carreg Gwalch to produce this book has again been a pleasure.

Margaret Hughes

Further Reading

Kyffin Williams, *Across the Strait.*

Y Bywgraffiadur Cymraeg hyd at 1940.

Margaret Hughes, *Crime and Punishment in Beaumaris.*

University of Wales Bangor Undergraduate Prospectus.

Cyfarwyddiadur Eglwysi Agored Esgobaeth Bangor (Directory of Open Churches Bangor Diocese).

Margaret Hughes, *Anglesey from the Sea.*

Môn Mam Cymru, The Guide to Anglesey (Magma Press).

H.R. Davies, Board of Celtic Studies, University of Wales, History and Law Series No. 8: *The Conway and Menai Ferries.*

Transactions, Anglesey Antiquarian Society & Field Club.

T. Meirion Hughes, *The Ferries to Anglesey*, Yesterday Series.

Ucheldre Centre, Holyhead: *Visitors Guide 2002.*

Ed. W. Eifion Jones, *The Natural History of Anglesey.*

Magma Press, *The Marram Weavers of Newborough.*

Constance Davies, *A Grain of Mustard Seed.*

Frances Lynch, *Prehistoric Anglesey.*

F.H. Glazebrook, *Anglesey and North Wales Coast.*

Geraint I.L. Jones, *Anglesey Railways.*

North Wales Wildlife Trust leaflet: *Mariandyrys.*

John Rowlands, *Copper Mountain.*

E.A. Williams (transl. G. Wynne Griffith), *The Day Before Yesterday.*

George Borrow, *Wild Wales.*

Margaret Hughes, *Anglesey Remembers*, *Anglesey Villages*, *Anglesey Lighthouses and Lifeboats*, *A-Z of Anglesey.*

Cyngor Gwynedd, *Tywysogion Gwynedd.*

J.L. Williams, *Llanfair Pwllgwyngyll.*

Anglesey Federation of W.I., *Millenium Memories.*

The Oxford Encyclopedia of Music.

Sir Llywelyn Turner, ed. Vincent; *Memoirs.*